This book is dedicated to all those who have a genuine desire to embrace the challenge of change, and who recognise that change always brings opportunity.

One

Bradley stood back, admiring his work on the wall, before returning to his green buttoned leather swivel chair. As he sat down he pulled himself forward towards the executive style desk with its matching green leather top and inlaid gold border.

He no longer felt threatened by that desk. The telephone to his left or the over full in-tray to the right. Even the daily 'things to do' list, mottled with red underlines and the numbers in the margin indicating the actions of highest priority no longer gave him that aching feeling deep in the pit of his stomach. He had often visualised that the ache was caused by his boss reaching inside his body and holding on with a vice like grip, exercising his authority and exerting his control.

Never again would he twitch and break out in a cold sweat as a knock on the door undoubtedly signified another problem on its way to the over worked in-tray.

Infact, he was quite looking forward to working his way down the list, seeking solutions to the various problems that each innocuous bullet point would undoubtedly lead to.

Their power to intimidate him had been dissolved, just like pieces of ice in a glass of beer, their seemingly invincible forms were nothing more than temporary obstacles. He removed his diary from his breast pocket and turned to the relevant page. January 2nd 1996. This was going to be a year with a difference. Never again would the start of another year be synonymous with pain, anguish and dread as it summoned the start of yet another year of frustration and challenge.

In previous years, the date on the calendar, and the same old films on television, always insisted that a new year had started, but the monotony of his life provided solid evidence to argue against them. What was the point in recognising and rejoicing in the start of another new year when he knew it would be just the same, if not worse, than the last one.

Another year filled with constant change. So many things would be different in so many ways, but his own inability to cope with those changes led him to the conclusion that nothing would really change at all - at least not in his world. Not in his inner world where time stood still and he lived in his memory.

He lived in a time when he could cope. A time when he was in control, and his thirst for knowledge guaranteed that he could always capitalise on the changes, embrace the new opportunities that they presented and use them to his benefit. It wasn't even so long ago, he didn't even see it coming, but practically overnight he had turned into a non-achiever.

He had regressed from a point where he used to live out of his imagination to a point where he now lived out of his memory. Looking back at his diary he smiled. He was pleased it was a two year diary and he leafed backwards through the pages to that fateful day only a few short weeks ago. A day that would surpass any other day that he had previously earmarked with that symbolic idea of a 'blue ribbon'. This day beat them all, and whilst he did now expect to have many successful, rewarding and fulfilling days in the future, none would replace the day he met Elizabeth.

As her name flashed across his mind every nerve in his body began to tingle. A shiver ran down his spine and he swallowed hard as he looked up at the picture he had hung on the wall just minutes ago. He wiped a tear from the corner of his eye and clenched his hands beneath his chin to make a platform for his head to rest upon.

When he left her this morning he knew he would never see her again. They both knew. The inevitable day had arrived.

In many ways, and to many onlookers, it would have seemed inconceivable that such a short and unlikely friendship could have had such a dramatic impact upon his life. In those few short days together, Elizabeth's zest for life, in a life destined to be so short and predictable, would stay with him for the rest of his days.

He pushed himself away from the desk, the casters of the chair making a muffled squeaking sound as they carved furrows out of the deep pile carpet. He couldn't resist returning to the wall again and he ran his fingers over the wooden picture frame as the urge to remember overtook his urge to return to his daily task list.

Two

Elizabeth awoke early that morning. It was unusually mild for the time of year and she was looking forward to spending several hours in the garden. She felt so fortunate to be alive, so thankful for the forces of nature that had not only created her but created everything in this beautiful garden that surrounded her. The fabulous array of flowers, their dazzling colours and their life sustaining nectar.

She was lost in her thoughts that morning and didn't see the stranger creeping up behind her, and that momentary loss of concentration was enough for him to enact his plan. Suddenly she was surrounded. She couldn't move for more than two or three inches in any direction, her field of vision was restricted and a dark shadow blotted out the early morning sunlight. She began to fight frantically as her natural defence mechanism kicked into gear but she feared it was too late. She hadn't been paying attention, hadn't been alert to the dangers of a predator and was sure that this momentary lapse was about to lead to her untimely death.

In one last attempt to save herself she shouted out. "Hey, let me go you big bully. Go and pick on someone your own size you coward."

She listened intently hoping for a response. An opportunity to talk to her captor, maybe negotiate with him and lower his guard then she could make a break for it before it was too late. There was no response, infact it was quieter than before. She could no longer hear the heartbeat of her assailant. "Let me go you over grown oaf, I'm no use to you, why do you want to capture me? Talk to me you idiot."

"To kill you of course." Bradley replied cautiously, looking over his shoulder to make sure there was no one else around, "to kill you."

"Why ? What harm am I likely to do to you ?" She began to feel more confident sensing an opportunity to strike up a conversation and get this guy to feel sorry for her.

"You don't fool me," Bradley snapped, "butterflies can't talk, it's just my sub conscious mind playing tricks on me. It does it all the time when I kill a spider or accidentally run over a rabbit even though I do my best to swerve and avoid them. You don't fool me at all boy, you can't talk and I'm going to kill you."

"Don't call me boy. I'm not a boy I'm a girl, and anyway what do you know about butterflies except how to sneak up on them? I bet you're the kind of guy that's always creeping around, sneaking up on people, cornering them for hours on end and boring the life out of them with your irrelevant stories and stupid hobbies. Infact, instead of threatening to kill me please get on with it, you're boring me already, I don't know how much more of this I can stand."

"Boring you, I'm boring you? I'm a human being, the finest of all Gods creations the manifestation of his unique creative powers, and I'm boring you !"

"Pathetic isn't it?" Elizabeth replied as she continued to goad Bradley. "It's so sad to see this so called 'ultimate creation' resorting to catching poor, innocent, defenceless butterflies in a net. Pathetic."

Elizabeth began to laugh as she sensed that her plan was starting to work. As Bradley became more annoyed his attention would drift and his hand that held the net would begin to move. One more insult should do it. "If you're so clever how come you don't know you've just torn your sleeve on the rose bush?" Bradley looked down and raised his hand slightly to bring his sleeve into full view. Sunlight poured onto the rose bush as the net lifted and Elizabeth fluttered her wings gliding off majestically, landing on a bright yellow carnation well out of Bradley's reach.

Bradley glanced all around him, shielding his eyes from the sunlight thrashing his net around in all directions in a vain attempt to recapture his quarry. He soon realised it was pointless and retreated down the garden to sit on the edge of the patio wall and ponder on the power of the subconscious mind.

It was quite clear to him that his natural dislike of harming animals had manifested itself in a life like fashion, acting as a kind of 'alter ego', and he resigned himself to the fact that it was perhaps for the best. He would no doubt have felt guilty for days after, just like the time when he ran over a hedgehog.

As he sat deep in thought the silence was punctuated by the sound of laughter. Female laughter he reasoned as he shook his head as if to send his subconscious thoughts back from whence they came. It was however to no avail, the laughing continued and started to get louder and closer. It was a laughter he had heard before.

"I bet you don't feel so superior now you big oaf."

Bradley shook his head once again, this time in disbelief as Elizabeth continued. "The oldest trick in the book and you fell for it hook line and sinker.

Anyway I've already alerted all my friends to the fact that you're creeping around the garden like some big white hunter after a priceless prey, so you can forget any hopes of catching another butterfly here today. You may as well go and wash your car instead, then you can drown some innocent spider that's made a nest in the exhaust pipe.

Better still you could go on a safari and shoot an elephant, maybe you'd have more success with something as big and clumsy as you."

A smile came to Bradley's face. He didn't know what was going on but she was right, if he couldn't catch a butterfly he may as well wash the car, infact all things considered he may as well talk to a butterfly !

"It's no use catching an elephant because I haven't got a picture frame large enough to put it in, and even if I had I wouldn't have a wall strong enough to hang it on."

"So you wanted to frame me and hang me on your wall. I've been told that humans had a fascination with that kind of thing but I've never understood why. Please tell me, why?"

Bradley thought for a minute. He wasn't really sure why, but he couldn't blame everything on his subconscious so maybe the process of answering the question would help him to frame his thoughts.

"I'm not a collector," he began, "so I can't speak for those guys that are, but from my own point of view I think It's probably because you symbolise freedom. You flit around from flower to flower drinking nectar and absorbing the sunlight without a care in the world. You don't have to go to work, sit in traffic jams, stand in supermarket queues, answer the telephone, clear the in-tray and deal with the trade unions. You're not a victim of change, a lost soul in an anonymous faceless society obsessed with materialism and new technology. You're not stressed out. You've got time to smell the roses.

I thought that by framing you and hanging you on the wall it would cheer me up. At times when I felt chained to my desk and imprisoned by my life I could look up at you and revitalise my vision of freedom. You would symbolise the day when I'm no longer required to undergo anymore psychological growth, I would know enough to never have to learn anything else, a time when I could choose to live the way I wanted to live, a time of freedom, a time of retirement."

Elizabeth gave a heavy sigh as she lowered her voice, feeling compelled to reply, but what could she say to this pathetic misguided individual who looked forward to the day when he wouldn't have to grow and change anymore.

A time when he had a stress free life. He obviously didn't realise he was describing the state of death - not retirement.

"I'm flattered kind sir." She began softly but wondered how long her patience would last. "I'm flattered that you think a casual glance at my scant frame and multi coloured wings, stretched out on a piece of card could summon up such emotions and feelings of optimism for some future time when your life will be perfect. However, as flattered as I am, my over riding emotion is anger. Minutes ago you told me what a wonderful creation you were, God's finest creation infact. You have such great abilities, such a capacity to invent things, build things, generate great wealth, out think the most advanced computers, and yet you require a casual glance at a dead butterfly to give you inner peace. Along with your capacity to achieve great things God has obviously also endowed you with an equally great capacity to achieve nothing.

A capacity to forsake your natural talents and abilities and subordinate them to other individuals allowing them to take control of your life.

I feel angry because you talk about freedom as if it is something that is only attainable when you are in a state of total paralysis, you use the word so readily to describe a euphoric state that you hope to aspire to one day. You have no perception of what the greatest freedom is, and no comprehension of the fact that you already have that freedom.

I feel angry because you not only live in a world of change, which you complain about, but your world of change is balanced by choice. My world is one of change without choice. It should be me who has you stuffed and mounted and hung on the garden fence. Then I can get enthused and inspired by the thought that one day I may reach a time in my life when I have choice over the changes that I undergo during my growth and development."

Bradley sat silently and motionless, in shock from the unexpected tirade. Maybe he should have washed the car after all. He started to backtrack on the things she had said, desperately searching for some key phrase that would help him to understand. Some point of reference to work from.

Three

He sensed they hadn't really got off on the right foot so maybe it was time to take a step back. "I'm Bradley what's your name?"

"I'm Elizabeth, pleased to meet you Bradley."

"Likewise," said Bradley as he finally pinpointed the rose bush that she was nestling in. "What kind of butterfly are you Elizabeth?"

"I'm a Peacock butterfly. I'm quite easy to identify because I have a most unusual wing design with 'peacock eye' marks on each wing, which is actually unique among all butterflies. I can be found anywhere across southern and central Europe from the British Isles eastwards to Asia and even further still to Japan. My species has even been known to go almost all the way to the Arctic Circle."

Bradley focused on the rose bush again until he could clearly see the 'peacock eyes' and the beautiful array of colours that adorned Elizabeth's wings. "You are truly a beautiful specimen Elizabeth, I'm so glad I didn't capture you after all."

"That makes two of us," replied Elizabeth, "but I'm glad we met because I do enjoy a bit of ready wit and repartee in between meals. I was in the garden of an eminent Psychologist for a few days last week and he was conducting a series of extra curricular classes in the early evenings for a few select students who asked for some additional material. It was fascinating to listen to their debates but I didn't join in because there were too many of them and I felt a little self conscious and vulnerable. If they had suddenly decided to capture me it would have been more difficult to escape."

"Is that where you got your strong views from?" Bradley asked.

"Not entirely," she replied without hesitation. "I've always had views on certain things but it did give me confirmation that some of the ideas that I valued were actually shared by other people, particular when we start to talk about an individuals ability or even responsibility to embrace change and to take control of their lives."

Bradley sensed he was being drawn back into the previous discussion, so that she could give him another verbal battering, but considered it was worth the risk. His powers of recall started to remind him of her earlier comments as he decided to dive headlong into the 'Peacocks den'.

"You said my world of change was balanced with choice, but yours was just a world of change, what did you mean by that Elizabeth?"

"Contrary to one of your earlier statements Bradley, where you said I 'wasn't a victim of change', I am infact the ultimate victim of change. My life, from the egg to the caterpillar to the chrysalis to the butterfly is synonymous with your life. It is one of inevitable change and constant challenge. We were both conceived to change, born to change, we live to change and we ultimately die to change. It is a natural process, the natural order of things. We are designed, built and engineered to change. The difference is that you have a choice in how you change and I have none. In our formative stage of life we both accepted change readily and looked forward to it with hope and optimism. As an embryo, inside the egg, we start to take on our genetic heritage and develop some of our basic characteristics from our parents.

Here the lifelong change process begins. Our bodies start to form, small and weak at first, but gradually growing in strength and size, to a point where we can support our own weight. We can survive without the cosseted environment of our protective shells, in your case the womb and in mine the egg.

I remember when I eventually became strong enough to break out of my egg. I didn't know what was on the other side of it, but sensed that I couldn't stay there any longer. I had outgrown it.

My jaws were now tough enough and I began to munch through the top of the egg. I rested periodically because this was the first opportunity I had to use my muscles.

The action of fighting my way out of the egg would give them the necessary strength to help me to survive in those first few vital days outside the egg. Once I emerged I was faced with a strange new world. It was fascinating and intriguing but also scary and hostile. My natural instincts, my genetic heritage, told me to seek cover, hide away safely and start to eat and to build my strength and size. At this stage I'm a caterpillar, a baby, black and spiny with white spots and I love to eat nettles. In my naiveté, just like a human baby, I think I have arrived.

This is how I was meant to be and this is how I will stay - my final form. My view of my life is a very simple one.

My frame of reference, my paradigm of my world, based upon my early experience, gives me no cause for concern. I do feel a little vulnerable but the more nettles I eat the bigger I get and the more confident I feel. It is of course false confidence because I tend to spend my time with other caterpillars, as you would other babies and children, and I compare and contrast my physical size to them.

Some are much smaller and less confident whilst some are bigger and supremely confident. Curiously enough there is also the odd contradiction. A small one that is very self assured and a large one that is self conscious. I ponder that maybe size alone is not the key, but why trouble my mind with such deep thoughts when it's time to have some fun, after all, I'll never experience a situation where I feel self conscious so it doesn't matter.

I'm unaware that there is mortal danger in the garden until one day the caterpillar of a lobster moth is skilfully removed from a nearby leaf by a huge flying thing, I now know to be called a bird. The only evidence of his existence is a hole in the leaf he was munching on only seconds earlier. I am suddenly more aware than ever before that life has its challenges. For you this realisation may have come with the death of a school friend in a car accident, the loss of an ageing relative or a household pet.

Whatever form this carrier of change takes, it has arrived in our life and we never forget it. Neither of us is sure where our friend or relative has gone, but as the days pass we realise they are not coming back.

I now have the motivation to learn, survival is my motivation. I learn that some caterpillars puff up the front of their bodies and show off false eyes to look like a snake and scare the birds away. I learn that some spray a nasty smelling liquid into the face of would be predators and I learn how to use my spines to their best effect.

In just the same way the human infant has the motivation to learn how to survive. He cries when he's hungry, smiles and looks cute when he requires attention and knows that when he touches the hot fire it hurts.

We both embark on our journey through life. A journey that begins with change, welcomes the opportunity to grow and embraces the challenge to learn. As a caterpillar I was Liz, far too naive and inexperienced to be Elizabeth, but Liz, a fun loving, inquisitive, optimistic, energetic self assured caterpillar.

I was happy in my ignorance as every day brought a new adventure and a new opportunity to learn, grow and change. I was full of dreams, ideas of things I wanted to achieve, places I wanted to visit. Dreams of long summer days lying in the sunshine and eating as many fresh nettles as I could manage. I also dreamt of one day bringing my own caterpillars into the world so that I could pass on the many things that I was learning about life. My appetite for new experiences grew by the day and I had an insatiable desire to learn. I didn't have a care in the world. I was Liz, and I was proud of it."

"I know what you mean, Bradley interrupted. When I was a young boy I felt indestructible. I felt as though I could go anywhere, do anything and still be back home for tea.

I dreamt of being a great football player, scoring a winning goal in the world cup and driving away from the

18

stadium in my red Ferrari. My destination was my apartment at the marina and a champagne reception on my yacht.

Happy naive memories Elizabeth. I really thought that's how my life would be. What a joy it would be to have another chance."

As Bradley dreamed of days gone by Elizabeth sat patiently and resisted the temptation to explain to him that his life could still be so different. To explain to him that no one needs a second chance, they simply need to understand a few basic principles to help them take full advantage of their first and only chance. More of that later, she was just getting to an interesting part of her own life.

Elizabeth flew a little closer, this time nestling in the heart of a daffodil and taking a drink of its nectar before continuing on.

"One day I noticed that I wasn't really growing out of my skin anymore. I used to shed it regularly and looked forward to each occurrence with its hidden benefits of increased self esteem. I seemed to have stopped growing all together in a physical sense and I had a strange feeling that my world was about to take an irreversible change.

This time the onset of change felt more uncomfortable than before. I didn't have a boost of self esteem to help me through it, and consequently I wasn't as confident about my ability to cope with it. I suddenly found myself yearning for the return of those long hot summer days and the carefree existence that I had come so accustomed to.

I feared I was on the verge of maturity, adulthood and responsibility. I'd expected it to feel differently. I didn't think I would be scared and unsure, less optimistic and less positive, but I was just that. Before I knew it I was a chrysalis, cocooned in a sort of no mans land a state of consciousness, but inactivity, a cross roads. The road behind me would be synonymous with your childhood years. The road in front with your adult years and where the two crossed, with choice.

Unbeknown to me at that time Bradley, this is where the similarities in our lives begin to diverge."

Four

"Once I came to terms with the fact that those childhood days were over, I understood I had a responsibility to give back to the world a part of what I had so innocently taken. I honestly thought that I would be able to choose the way I would fulfil that responsibility. I had spent my youth as a caterpillar observing the various different types of butterflies. Their personalities, their method of operation and their role in nature. Whilst I didn't fully realise that I would end up being a butterfly, I felt a great affinity with their form, a natural bonding that felt very special.

I used to play a game, a mind game not unlike your 'dreaming' game. I used to think about what kind of butterfly I would like to be, or choose to be, if ultimately I had the opportunity to become one.

From my observations I realised there were several thousand variations or species to choose from and it would be impossible to make a well thought out choice. I decided instead to characterise and categorise them by their habitat, the place in which they lived because I realised that said a great deal about their personality, their inner self. Their likes and dislikes and most importantly their ability to deal with change. Don't forget that all these thoughts were going on in my mind whilst sat in my cocoon, convinced that I had the power to choose the way I would think and act. How wrong I was to assume that I had that power of choice, and how wrong you are to assume that you do not. I observed that there were essentially six key habitats to choose from:

the garden
the woodland
the mountains
the rainforest
the desert
the Arctic

As I describe the personalities, strengths and weaknesses that are attached to each of these habitats and their inhabitants it will be interesting to see if you think they resemble some of the kinds of human personalities that you have observed.

The garden   is filled with colourful sweet-smelling flowers and attracts a large number of butterflies by day and moths by night. In the summer you'll see caterpillars attacking leaves, moths hiding in trees and butterflies sunbathing on flowers. The Brimstone moth is a familiar garden visitor that hides by day and flies by night. A frequent visitor is the Comma butterfly, and he typifies the mentality of the garden dwellers. He is a master of disguise, and at the slightest sign of impending danger or change he will turn into the vision of an old brown leaf.

He's a pacifist and his way of dealing with change would be to simply give in and go along with it. Some would argue that this is not a bad attitude to take, after all keeping your head down and just letting things happen certainly reduces the stress levels. I would be the first to agree that on occasion there will be situations that you cannot change no matter how hard you try, and at those rare times it is indeed prudent to give in.

At times you could even consider it a strength. To be able to step down, acknowledge the change, embrace it and move on regardless, living to fight another day. As a way of life however, It's a sure fire way to guarantee a growing inability to cope with ongoing change, and an increasing feeling of frustration. Ultimately there will come a time when the Comma has to fight for his survival and he will be so used to giving in that this pacifist style will lead to his ultimate downfall !

Therefore, whilst I would not hesitate to visit the garden on the odd occasion that it was prudent to do so, I could never live there.

The woodlands are one of the best places to find butterflies and moths. You'll find them all around you, fluttering on flowers in sunny glades, resting on twigs and branches or even hiding under leaves on the ground.

On hot summer days look for the Purple Hairstreaks and Silver-washed fritillaries near oak trees. The oak leaf Roller caterpillar lives inside a rolled up leaf. When ants threaten to attack it spins a silk thread so that it can dangle off the leaf and out of danger.

The more typical characters in the woodlands are the Eggfly butterfly and the Heath fritillary. The Eggfly can be spotted in many different countries including Australia and North America. It is very fussy and only lives on sunny woodland edges and clearings.

Similarly, the Heath fritillary loves the sun and it hardly moves at all in dull weather, only putting in an appearance when conditions are perfect. When faced with change therefore, the style of these perfectionists is to totally ignore it. Whilst the Comma butterfly chooses to accept the change and get on with it, the Heath fritillary rejects the change and avoids it. This response is born out of a great desire for everything to be perfect all the time, and change represents the likelihood of imperfection - a situation they could not tolerate.

Again this outlook can be both a strength and a weakness. There is every sense in avoiding change for the sake of it, and anyone who is implementing change should always begin with the simple question 'will this change cause improvement?' The implementation of a new system or a new organisational structure isn't always the solution to the problems of a business. Their problems may go much deeper and may even lie at the roots of the business - it's founding principles and ideas, the way it treats its employees and so on. Perhaps the most frustrating consequence of the perfectionist style is that it makes no effort towards co-operation or partnership and as such adds nothing to the overall team effort. It is for the most part very selfish and I would find myself a very infrequent visitor to The woodlands.

The mountains have quickly changing weather with dark clouds, snow flurries and high winds appearing out of nowhere in minutes. You'll find the poisonous Monarch butterfly in the lowlands as well as on the tops of mountains. The small Apollo butterfly has greasy wings that mean it can survive freezing weather and sudden snow flurries. Many mountain insects survive the cold by sunbathing during the day, trapping the heat in black spots on their wings to keep them warm at night.

As we visit the mountains we see that nothing is hardier and more stubborn than the Burnet moth. You can find this red and black survivor in the mountains of central America, Asia and Europe. It tastes so bad that birds spit it out immediately, leaving large numbers of these moths to survive and breed. It has learned to cope with the changing environment of the mountains through sheer resistance and stubbornness. It fights change at every opportunity constantly objecting to its presence in any shape or form. This attitude of objecting can be a very positive position to take when under threat in a hostile environment and ensures that those around you know exactly where you stand.

However, there is a very destructive and negative downside to this type of approach to change. It totally denies any possibility that the change may be for the good and as such could very easily disregard a great opportunity to move forward and prosper, because of it's blinkered one sided approach.

I could see myself getting a great deal of benefit from visiting the mountains when I had to resist a damaging change at all costs, but I would find it a much too harsh and negative environment to pay it anymore than a flying visit.

The desert provides an interesting habitat. You won't see many butterflies or moths flying around during the day because it's too hot. The best time to watch for them is in the morning or in the evening and at midday you will most likely find a Tiger Blue resting under a rock.

You can also look for them flying around water holes where grasses and wild flowers grow. It is essential that they find water every day and have been known to take drinks from animal droppings to get that all important moisture.

As the sun sets in the Australian desert the large Ghost moth flies around in search of food. It's light colours and long wings make it look like a scary phantom. The interesting thing about living in the desert is the way that the inhabitants co-operate with each other and with nature. A butterfly may be patient and wait for the rain to fall before it emerges from its pupa, even if that process takes several years !

After hatching, caterpillars of the Yucca Skipper butterfly work as a team to tie the leaves of the Yucca together with silk. They then live together in harmony feeding on the leaves, safely hidden from predators. Their way of dealing with change is the way of enthusiastic co-operation. They don't make things happen, but they welcome the fact that things are happening, and choose the way of compromise to find the best route through the change.

This is a fairly safe way to ensure that you at least get some say in what's happening, even though you may ultimately have to abide by a group decision that is not wholly to your liking.

The desert would be a place I would visit regularly but it still doesn't cater for my desire to have more control over the outcome of the changes that act upon me.

The rainforest is like no other place on earth with the variety of colourful butterflies and moths that can be found there. Plentiful rainfall and a variety of plants make it an ideal home. The best places to spot butterflies are sunny areas by riverbanks, in clearings and around flowers. Male butterflies have to drink lots of water that is rich in salts so they can make special scents to attract us females and you can often see the Nero butterfly searching deep into the damp sand to find water.

Here the butterflies are particularly flamboyant and very aggressive, seeming to have more than their fair share of confidence. The flashy Malachite is only too glad to show off his form, whilst the Uranid moth cockily purports to look and indeed fly like a butterfly. Many of the rainforest caterpillars live in groups with the idea that the bigger the group, the safer they are. However, that reasoning doesn't stop them growing poisonous spines and horns.

They are resilient and resourceful and will, when faced with change, adopt it, make it theirs and do their best to make it happen.

Sadly they don't have the finesse of a less abrasive or more subtle operator and whilst they mean well their methods can be somewhat intimidating and uncaring.

You wouldn't describe them as leaders, but you would certainly want them on your team .If I were to choose a second home it would most certainly be in the rainforest.

The Arctic is a place where it is very difficult to withstand the freezing winters, strong winds and short summers, but a few butterflies and moths live there all year round. They have special survival features such as antifreeze in their blood, and dark colours to absorb heat quickly.

When temperatures fall below zero Arctic chrysalis remain safely protected inside silk cocoons. The Arctic Clouded Yellow butterfly flies when the sun is shining and has long hairs on his body to keep him warm. To make the most of this weak sunshine the Sooty Ringlet stretches its wings across a warm rock and lifts its body in the air to maximise heat absorption. The butterflies of the Arctic are very resourceful and besides finding ways to keep warm they are constantly challenged to avoid the multitude of predators - there are many hungry birds and spiders. Most Arctic moths and butterflies spend their nights making low, short flights from flower to flower, checking on their friends, and feeding as they go.

I would describe these butterflies as leaders. Their way of dealing with change is proactive acceptance. In other words they embrace it, and not only help to bring it about but also adapt it and channel it in the most positive way for the overall benefit of them all.

The Arctic butterfly does infact have the sense to use whichever style is necessary to gain the greatest benefit from any impending change. It has the ability to be proactive, to actually anticipate and bring about change and rely on its imagination to see the positives from the change, rather than being reactive and making its decisions based on past events.

You've probably guessed it already Bradley, but I'll say it anyway, the Arctic is where I would have chosen to be, if I'd had a choice."

The second that Elizabeth stopped talking she plunged her head deep into the centre of an adjacent flower and took a long, well deserved drink. Bradley sat silently, almost in awe at what he had just heard. She had said, before she began explaining the various habitats and their inhabitants, it would be interesting to see if he thought they resembled some of the human personalities that he had observed. He hardly thought that 'interesting' was an appropriate word to describe what had amounted to a one hundred percent correlation with the various ways in which he himself had responded to the various changes in his own life over the years.

Some he had accepted, some he had ignored, some he helped to cause, some he had aggressively fought against, others he had aggressively fought for, and some he had created and implemented .On reflection he had to admit that his predominant styles in recent years had been those of acceptance or avoidance. Using her terminology he had spent many hours sitting in the garden or hiding in the woodlands .What's more he was embarrassed to admit that he too would like to 'live in the Arctic'.

"You've given me many things to think about Elizabeth." Will I have the chance to speak with you again?"

Elizabeth laughed as she answered. "You bet, I've still got to tell you about the greatest discovery I have ever made.

It took a great deal of changing before I became Elizabeth, or at least the Elizabeth that I was happy to be. Now I must fly. Bye for now Bradley".

Five

That evening, after supper, Bradley sat in front of the huge open fire in the lounge and gazed aimlessly into its hypnotic flames. As the minutes passed by it became easier to rationalise what had happened to him that afternoon. He was obviously more stressed than he had even realised. He had read about how the mind will find creative ways in which to warn you of impending danger.

He could only conclude that he was being warned to slow down before he had a nervous breakdown His subconscious was delivering a message to him that he must not ignore.

He sipped on his glass of red wine as he recalled several recent articles that described in detail how the odd glass of red wine had a therapeutic effect on the body and could actually ward of illness and increase longevity. This pleased him because he'd always liked the odd bottle and now he could justify it on medical grounds.

Slowly the uncoordinated pattern of the roaring flames started to take on a more definite order and he began to

31

focus on the newly emerging picture. It was a much younger Bradley. It was Brad, sat in the career's classroom at his old comprehensive school.

To his left his mother sits quietly whilst to his right his father is talking to the grey haired personnel guy from the local engineering company.

"Don't you worry about a thing Mr Jackson. Our Bradley was born to be an engineer, it's in his blood. His grandad was an engineer, his brothers are engineers and I'm an engineer. He's grown up with it. I've been preparing him for it for years. From the time I built him a train track for Christmas to the time I let him build his own tree house and the time when I selected his options for him at school. Don't you worry, he's a natural."

So it was, another in a long line of engineers from the Robert's family. He didn't argue or complain, it was his father's dream for him to get an engineering apprenticeship and have a better start in life than he had.

He wanted Bradley to get a trade, a secure job, was that so wrong of him?

Probably not, after all his father knew what it was like to be out of work. To live on the bread line and to suffer the humiliation of the dole queues, so you couldn't argue with his motives, but what about Bradley. What did he want. He wanted to be an entrepreneur, a businessman, a creator of business and opportunity. He wanted to be more than just an employee. He had so many dreams inside him. So many things he wanted to do and achieve, so many places he wanted to visit, so many ideas he wanted to try out, so many aspirations for the future but so little confidence to express himself to his father.

In the words of Elizabeth he had chosen to visit the Garden. He was in his chrysalis, 'cocooned', as she put it 'in a sort of no mans land. A state of consciousness but inactivity, a cross road'. The road behind - his childhood, the road in front - adulthood, and he was sat at that cross-roads of choice. He pondered that his real choice in this situation hadn't been the choice to grow up or not, that wasn't really an option, his choice had been between his father's aspirations or his own.

He chose his father's, he chose to live in the garden He chose to give in and go along with the change. He remembered Elizabeth saying she would not hesitate to visit the garden on the odd occasion that it was prudent to do so but she could never live there.

Suddenly a shiver ran down Bradley's spine as he came to the shattering conclusion that he had up to this point in his life chosen to live there. The path it seemed had been laid out on that wet and windy Autumn day in the classroom and it was now up to him to make the best of it. Bradley snapped out of his trance as a hot splinter of coal was ejected from the heart of the fire and with expert accuracy found the bare skin between his sock and his trouser leg.

He recharged his glass of red wine on the basis that it was the only way he would get any sleep, and retired to bed.

The following morning he awoke with an irritating itch on his nose. He lashed out in a semiconscious state hoping it was a fly and not a wasp.

"Hey, that's no way to treat a lady. Are you always this grumpy in the mornings? It's six thirty and the sun is shining. Wake up I want to talk to you".

Bradley jumped up sending the continental quilt soaring towards to ceiling. He gathered his thoughts and tried desperately to focus as the first rays of sunlight pierced the gap in the curtains.

"You left the window open last night. You should be careful about doing that there's a lot of petty crime around these days you know. The way you were sleeping someone could have emptied the house and you wouldn't even have noticed".

"Good morning Elizabeth, thanks for the lecture." Bradley acknowledged her presence as he reached over and took a long drink from the glass of water beside his bed.

The medical journals omitted to mention the headaches and dehydration associated with an over enthusiastic approach to their new non-prescription medication from Bordeaux.

He dressed and invited Elizabeth to join him on the patio for breakfast. She accepted readily on the condition that she could have a small saucer of the sweetest jam he could find. Bradley agreed and the high powered breakfast meeting began.

He told her about his previous evenings' recollections of his initiation into employment and she listened patiently, tutting occasionally as if to say 'yes, that's par for course, nothing new there buster'. As he finished she felt it appropriate to carry on with her own story.

"As I look around your lovely home Bradley I have to agree that your father at least guided you down a road that has brought some success, at least in a material sense. I do however detect an inner feeling of dissatisfaction that you can maybe tell me about later.

For my own part I was looking forward to emerging from my cocoon as an Arctic butterfly, an Arctic clouded Yellow butterfly. I love yellow. In my cocoon I was Beth.

I'd moved on from being Liz. I'd changed from being that carefree youth that had so many dreams for the future and such naive views on life. I now knew that I wouldn't be able to spend the rest of my days footloose and fancy free. As Beth I accepted that I had grown up a little. I had some emerging responsibilities but I was still very optimistic for the future. I still had dreams, although they were not quite as wild and crazy, they were tempered with the realities that I had experienced.

The loss of my friend when the bird captured him in the prime of his youth, the realisation that I would grow and change and the feelings that maybe things weren't as simple and straightforward as I had once imagined.

The funny thing is that whilst I mourned the passing of Liz, I embraced the arrival of Beth, and with it a new found maturity. A new outlook on life that was actually equally as exciting. . .I felt more in control of my surroundings because I felt that I had the freedom of choice. In many ways Beth was just as naive as Liz but she just didn't realise it yet. Where Liz was naive enough not to care about anything, Beth was naive enough to think she knew everything. That girl was in for a real shock! I'm not sure which is the more dangerous, not realising there's anything to know, or thinking you know everything. I imagine that there is a time when both these attitudes can be a strength and a time when both can be a weakness. Such, as they say, is life."

"When you were Liz I was Brat, a real brat." Bradley interrupted.

I resisted parental input at every turn. I had more independence when I knew nothing but thought I knew everything than I do now, as Bradley. Now I know many things, but realise I know nothing, and have more to learn now than I have ever learned up to this point in my life.

Shakespeare wrote that 'the fool thinks he is wise, but the wise man knows himself to be a fool'. I suspect that Brat and Liz were fools and Bradley and Elizabeth are becoming wise."

Elizabeth sat silently for several minutes before replying.

"I agree that in many ways Brat and Liz were fools, but it was an innocent foolishness. A foolishness born out of dreams of what life could be. A naive expectation that life was fair, constant and unvarying and a foolishness that always assumed they would be dealt an even hand. Sat in my cocoon as Beth, you were probably sat in your tree house as Brat. Yes, we had started to learn things, and yes we had our foolishness tempered with education and as we approached the cross roads that led to maturity we both had great hope for the future.

We are now approaching the time where our similarities are about to end Bradley." He now detected a great seriousness in her voice as she set the scene for what he expected to be a dose of wisdom far more potent and life enhancing than his favourite bedtime tipple.

"I emerged from my cocoon as Elizabeth. I had flourished into adulthood at last. The waiting was over, I had changed for the last time. No more hiding in the leaves from the birds, no more shedding my skin as I got fatter and no more crawling around on the floor. Now I had matured and the change process was complete.

The feeling was for the most part indescribable. Freedom to go, no, to fly wherever I wanted to. Freedom to drink of the nectar of any flower that I chose and freedom to start a family and perpetuate my species. What a wonderful feeling Bradley.

I took to the air, rising high above the branches that my cocoon had been suspended from. I felt warm and assumed that the antifreeze in my blood and my long hairs were doing their job of protecting me from the Arctic cold. I marvelled at how efficient they were because I had expected to at least feel a little cold, and I decided to test them to the full by landing on a snow capped peak.

I raised my head and began to look around, first in front, then to the left and right, then behind. I felt confused and uneasy. Where were the snow capped peaks, the strong winds, the below zero temperatures, the challenges that I had so looked forward to. Where was the familiar sight of the Sooty Ringlet stretched across the rock absorbing what little heat he could to sustain him through the long cold night ahead.   I stopped fluttering my wings and glided softly downwards as I tried to come to terms with my unexpected environment. I landed on a lily causing a ripple that distorted the surrounding water.

As the ripples radiated outwards the water began to settle and after a minute or so it was again perfectly still. I looked down into the water in disbelief. Where were my yellow wings? Who was I? What was I? Where was I?"

Six

"I sat there motionless for what seemed like an eternity. I was hoping I would wake up and find myself back in my cocoon. I had been impatient to leave Beth behind, I had wanted to grow up so quickly so that I would be in total control of my life, so that I would be free to live my life as I chose. What cruel trick had nature played on me? What had I done to deserve this?"

Bradley could no longer contain himself as he shouted out. "So you were in the garden, not the Arctic. The garden "

Elizabeth nodded as she continued. "Yes. I was in the garden. The place I least expected to be. The place I envisaged visiting on that rare occasion that I would have to accept someone else's plans for my life and go along with their decisions. I was like Brad in the careers interview, my life felt like it had ended. The crushing realisation that my fate had not really been in my hands at all. I had been dealt a bad hand, the deck had been stacked against me. All my hopes, dreams and aspirations crumbled in front of my very eyes. The reflection of a

Peacock butterfly in that lily pond told me all I needed to know and I wished I were dead."

An uneasy silence came over the garden as Elizabeth plunged her head deep into the saucer of 'extra fruit' strawberry jam.

Bradley felt such empathy that he couldn't contain himself. "I know how you felt", he blurted out loudly, then self consciously looked around to make sure that no one was watching.

"It was just the same when I began my apprenticeship. I had accepted that I was lucky to get a job. That provided I worked hard, studied hard and qualified as a tradesman I would never be unemployed and always have money in my pocket. True enough it was unlikely I would ever have the Ferrari or the yacht and riverside apartment, but I'd be better off than many. I had also learned a new word that I couldn't remember coming across in my childhood days. The word was compromise. I remember looking it up in the dictionary the first time I heard it.

Compromise, '.....settlement reached my making concessions on both sides.....'.

That's what I'd done. I made concessions by tempering my dreams with reality, that's what I'd done on my side, but I couldn't work out who had done what on the other side. Then one day, when I was sweeping the workshop floor for the third time, not because it was still dirty but because the instructor said it would teach persistence and discipline as an apprentice that would stay with me as a tradesman, it finally came to me.

The other side of the compromise was life itself. Life had struck a bargain with me. Life had also made some concessions, which ironically were the same as mine. I had compromised my hopes dreams and aspirations and chosen the line of least resistance and life itself had met me half way by choosing to also deny what it would have loved to give me - my hopes, dreams and aspirations - I had made a compromise with life itself."

Bradley too became silent as he relived that day when he finally recognised the existence of the power of the self fulfilling prophesy.

"You've got to be kidding." Elizabeth interrupted his deep thought.

"You moron. You figured that out over twenty years ago and yet you still live a life of compromise. You still live in the garden. There's another definition of compromise that suits you better, '...... to commit to a policy unwisely.....'.

Don't you understand?" Her frustration began to show as she fluttered her wings frantically and hovered above Bradley's head.

"The self fulfilling prophesy is like life itself. It's dynamic, it's constantly changing, just because you commit to a policy unwisely doesn't mean you're stuck with that policy. If it did it would mean you were a butterfly.

That's the difference between you and me. That's the difference between the human animal and every other animal. You are only a product of your environment if you choose to be so. I am a product of my environment whether I choose to be or not.

I didn't emerge from my cocoon as a Clouded Yellow. I emerged as a Peacock, and my path was set. You didn't emerge from your tree house as an entrepreneur, you emerged as an engineer - as a tradesman - but the only place that your path was set was in your mind. Earlier you gave me a quotation from Shakespeare. Well, I've sat in the gardens of his historical house, seen plays enacted in those gardens in the summertime and I've got a quotation for you buster, '....... Nothing is either good or bad, only thinking makes it so'.

You're a product of your environment for one very simple reason. Because thinking makes it so. I told you when we first met that I could be found anywhere across central Europe from the British Isles eastwards to Asia and even farther still to Japan. I also said my species has even been known to go almost all the way to the Arctic circle. Notice my words Bradley, notice them and never ever forget them. Almost, almost, almost all the way to the Arctic circle. I can never go there Bradley. I'm a product of my environment. I'm not equipped for that degree of change in climate - if I go there I will die.

That is not some fatalistic thought that I use to justify my laziness at not attempting to embark on such a long and strenuous journey.

I have tried Bradley. I have in past summers set out on that long hard journey. I have tried and I have failed but non the less I have tried. What if the naturalists had got it wrong and it was possible to find a colony of Peacock butterflies alive and well in the Arctic. I couldn't take the chance. I couldn't resign myself to a life in the garden until I was absolutely sure, convinced beyond any shadow of a doubt that I could not attain my youthful dreams, the dreams of Liz and Beth. The dreams of living in the Arctic. The dreams of being a butterfly capable of leading others and capable of setting the standard, taking the initiative and making a difference in the lives of others.

I had to know for sure. I had to find out for myself. The process almost killed me, and it was only when I stared death in the face, when I knew that I had given it my best shot, that I could return to the garden. Only when I had pushed myself as far as I could go, when I was cold, exhausted, hungry and defenceless, only then could I return to the garden and live a life of compromise.

It was only when I had refused to '..... commit to a policy unwisely', that I could eventually agree to a '...... settlement reached by making concessions on both sides'.

Only then could I make that compromise with nature. I finally understood and accepted that the self fulfilling prophesy was unique to the human animal - the rest of the animal kingdom was destined to compromise with nature itself. It is for this reason that I readily call you a moron Bradley.

Not out of malice or hatred, but out of love and frustration, that you do not embrace the one true freedom that is afforded every one of your species. The freedom of choice. The freedom to resist being a mere product of your environment.

The freedom to chose the person you want to be and the freedom to learn, grow and change into that person regardless of your surroundings. The freedom to be master of your circumstances rather than servant to them.

The freedom to choose the way that you see the world, regardless of the way the world sees you. The freedom of living to grow and growing to live....... and the freedom to go into the kitchen and get another saucer of that delicious strawberry jam for me."

Seven

They finished breakfast in silence, each deep in their own thoughts of the past, present and future. Bradley didn't mind being called a moron, he looked upon it more as a term of endearment than ridicule and understood that Elizabeth felt the need to use emotive language to get through to him.

He admired that she had done all in her power to pursue her lifelong dream of living in the Arctic and despaired that he had done so little to pursue his. It was undeniable that he had allowed his early compromise to set the pattern for his life. He didn't however feel entirely responsible for this situation because he had never really had the confidence to step outside of that compromise.

Reflecting on his agreement to begin an apprenticeship, as opposed to entering into his first business venture - a self assembly tree house kit - he came to the conclusion that the education system he had been enrolled into focused almost entirely on teaching him and guiding him towards being a 'something'. The problem was, he wanted to be a 'somebody'.

He had always rationalised this recurring thought by telling himself that the educators are really clever and they know that if they help you to become a 'something' you will automatically become a 'somebody'.

He didn't deny that there was a logic to this, but wondered how many times it actually worked out for the best. How many times' people ended up being a general 'something' rather than a meaningful specific 'somebody'.

The first time he could really remember experiencing a lesson about being a somebody was when he had started out on the route of being a something. When he became an engineering apprentice they started to teach him about persistence and determination - sweeping the clean floor three times, carrying his heavy toolbag home when he could have left it in the locker overnight, and so on.

Persistence and determination were about being a somebody. They weren't specific to being an apprentice, they were attitudes that were vital if he was to excel at anything, but he had never had that explained to him until he was a something.

Surely the key was to teach people to be a somebody, then they would be fully equipped to be an 'anything' not just a 'something' but an 'anything' they dreamed of being.

Elizabeth broke the silence. "So champ, are you ready to break free from the shackles of your environment ?"

Her question was very direct and for a moment Bradley found it difficult to come to terms with its inference. "I'm not quite sure what you mean Elizabeth. I'm not sure that I am shackled to my environment, and even if I am, maybe I like it."

She expected him to be defensive. It was only natural when someone had just been told that they had built their entire adult life based upon a compromise that they had little or no control over.

"Don't sulk Bradley," her mood was now merciless. "I'm not criticising you. You've made a success out of your life in many ways, but success in the past is no guarantee of success in the future. I'll make you a deal. If you can look me in the eye and tell me with all truth and sincerity that you will be happy to live the rest of your life travelling the path that you are currently on; that you no longer have a fire in your belly; that you do not have dreams that you would still like to pursue; that you are not prepared to fight against your self doubt and become the person that you want to be - a somebody as opposed to a something - I will fly away from this garden now and never return."

Bradley raised his head, looked her straight in the eye, as she had requested, swallowed hard and exercised his Freedom of choice. "Let's break the shackles."

Elizabeth smiled, and took a long drink from the strawberry jam before continuing. "When you meet a person for the first time in a social environment, what is the first thing you tell them about yourself?"

"That's obvious," Bradley replied, "I tell them my name."

"What's the second?" She continued. This time Bradley thought a little harder before replying.

"It depends upon the situation, but I suppose more often than not I tell them what I do for a job."

"Why?" Elizabeth didn't allow him to come up for air before the next question was delivered.

"Well, I suppose it's a way of entering into some kind of conversation. It's something to say until we can get onto more interesting things."

"And do you?" Again there was no chance to review his response before the next question arrived. "Do I what?" Bradley snapped, his irritation starting to show.

"Do you ever get onto more interesting things before the conversation dies and you move on to the next victim? The next recipient of your un-inspiring diatribe about engineering project management."

"Is there a point to these questions Elizabeth? I can sense that I'm getting annoyed with you but I can't understand why. What are you driving at?"

"Simple," she replied in a slightly patronising tone adopted purposely to ensure she got his full attention.

"Almost every human being that I have ever heard speak is obsessed with telling people about what he or she does - not who they are. Let's turn the question around for a minute.

If you were to ask someone what they did, so that you were on the receiving end of the answer and they were telling you what they did for a job, what thought process do you go through as they deliver their answer?"

"Well, I would listen, nod a couple of times and try to understand at least some of what they are telling me so that I can look for any aspect that I may know something about or that I can ask a question about."

"O.K. What else is going through your mind apart from searching for a common thread of understanding?"

Elizabeth was relentless in her questioning and Bradley assumed he hadn't yet given her the answer she was looking for.

"If I'm being honest about it I suppose I would be making an assessment of their income level, their level of intelligence, depth of education, sphere of influence, the type of home they live in and the type of car they drive."

"Good," she replied. "What else Bradley? What else?"

"I would start to make a comparison between what they did, my early perception of the kind of life they must lead and what I do, and the kind of life that I lead. I would also be preparing my thoughts to answer the same question when they ask it of me."

"Thank you Bradley." Elizabeth breathed a sigh of relief, having received the answer she was looking for, and began to explain her point.

"Most reference books on body language would seem to agree that ninety percent of your impression and opinion of someone is formed in the first ninety seconds, and once formed it can be a long arduous road to re-forming that impression. I'm not saying that you shouldn't tell people what you do for a living in those first ninety seconds, you may be very proud of it, you may feel that it describes you perfectly as a person and be happy to talk about it as soon as possible. What I am trying illustrate is that people form so many impressions, comparisons and assumptions based upon what we do as opposed to who we are."

"Put simply," Bradley interrupted, "they use the fact that we're a 'something', to form an opinion of what kind of 'somebody' we are."

"Exactly," exclaimed Elizabeth. "When someone asks you what you do it is to a large extent both a status enquiry and a basis to form an opinion about you as a person. I suggest that this is a very dangerous preoccupation because people think that if they know what you do, they know how to treat you. That is very sad because it often gives no real indication of the kind of person you actually are. You may be a square peg in a round hole.

An engineer that dreams of being an entrepreneur. A taxi driver that yearns to be an actor. A shop assistant that can't get a break as a musician. Nevertheless, people will treat you with a preconceived view of how to treat people that come from a background of the round hole, and not take time to find out what kind of square peg you actually are. The question we are raising here is one of perception. How you are perceived by both yourself and others? Is your occupation the thing that pays the bills or is it a true extension and reflection of what and who you are and how you think?. A job title doesn't scratch the surface of what you are and who you are, but it is used so many times to form those vital first impressions.

Depending upon your answer to the question, and the other persons thought processes based upon your answer, that could be the first and last time you speak to them or it could be the start of a wonderful and fulfilling friendship."

Bradley sat in deep thought and poured himself a cup of tea. He didn't seem to notice that it was cold and stewed, he was trying to unravel the web of words that Elizabeth had woven around this age old question of 'what do you do?' Eventually, and with great caution he was ready to deliver his most profound analysis of her lecture.

"So, what is really important is not what I do, but what I think about myself as a person while I'm doing it." He let out a deep sigh as he finished the sentence. He felt like a schoolboy waiting for the head teacher to mark his homework and impose detention for extra study.

"That's it," she replied, sounding almost as amazed as he looked stunned. "That's the first important aspect of change Bradley, and it's called perception.

It's about what you see when you look in the mirror. Do you see a project manager and all the aspects of that work combined to be your whole self? Do you see a man who has not achieved his boyhood dreams and is now resigned to a mundane existence? Do you see a person that is on the wrong side of forty, too old to learn new tricks or embrace the challenge of change? Why not look deeper? Beyond the surface of that reflection.

If you cannot see past the reflection in the mirror you will never be able to handle the changes that are coming your way. Look deeper Bradley, look deeper into yourself.

Look beyond that ninety second conversation with a stranger because in just the same way that it forms the basis of that relationship, you have that same ninety second conversation with yourself everytime you look into the mirror.

When the ripples settled on the pond and I sat motionless on that lily I couldn't comprehend my physical form. No yellow colouring. No long hairs to keep me warm on the snow capped peaks. No determined expression on my face. Inside, in my perception of myself, I was built for the Arctic, but on the outside I was camouflaged for the garden. I suggest that many people in this world are also camouflaged for the garden but deep inside themselves, hidden deep inside that two dimensional reflection they are built for the Arctic.

How sad it would be Bradley if we looked no farther than the reflection."

Elizabeth could see Bradley had enough to think about for the moment and she decided to take her leave. There was a particularly nice looking white flower at the bottom of the garden that was shielded from the sunlight. She considered that to be the perfect place to continue working towards her goal, and she glided majestically through the clear blue sky to the coldest place in the garden.

Bradley made some fresh tea and sat at the kitchen table making copious notes on the conversation just passed. He was writing in what he called his 'project book'. A small leather bound book that he used to sketch and plan out any jobs he had to do around the house. He smiled as he realised that even the book he used specifically for activities related to his home life had been named like one of his folders at work. He immediately reached into the kitchen cupboard and pulled out one of the sticky labels he used on the jam pots. He removed the label from its grease proof cover and stuck it onto the front of the book watching the words 'project book' slowly disappear. He then found his favourite gold marker pen and inscribed the new label with the word 'Imagineering'.

He sat back from the table as he wiped a tear from his eye. He felt totally silly to be in such an emotional state but he couldn't help it.

That simple word, now inscribed on the book for all eternity, summoned up such feelings of pride and enhanced self esteem. It was no longer a book that recorded the jobs that he did. It was a book that represented his spirit of creativity. The manifestation of his ideas and his imagination. No longer a two dimensional cover that reflected his occupation, it was a three dimensional monument to his inner self. That had to be worth a tear of joy at any time of the day.

Armed with his new perception of his book he began to leaf through its pages reviewing the designs that he had transformed into physical entities. The brick barbecue in the garden, the window seat in the lounge, the attic conversion and the picture frame.

The picture frame. He inserted his index finger into the pages, bringing the fanning motion to an abrupt halt, and opened the book up at the centre pages where he had drawn the design for Elizabeth's coffin. The picture frame was ten inches by eight inches by two inches deep. The front was made of non reflecting glass so that the sunlight would not affect the image whatever time of day he glanced over at it. The background was to be a pale yellow board with a small multi coloured border of flowers and the frame itself a fairly simple antique pine with two rebates down each edge.

As he ran his fingers over the pages it brought back memories of the first time he met Elizabeth in the garden, and in particular of the first question that she asked him. "....... why do you want to capture me?"

"To kill you of course," was his answer. He also recalled his reason for wanting to capture her and entomb her in his cleverly designed frame that was staring up at him from his Imagineering book.

Looking at the frame and its contents would cheer him up he had thought. It would summon up all kinds of emotions that lay deep inside him. Thoughts of retirement, freedom and a stress free existence. Suddenly he began to turn the pages rapidly to where he had been writing a few minutes earlier. The realisation of what was happening hit him straight between the eyes with the sting of a well placed fragment of hail stone, sending an icy shiver down his spine.

Looking at her form was intended to summon up all these emotions in him. Looking at his form summoned up emotions of frustration and entrapment. He could see the hidden depths in the butterfly but could not see the hidden depths in himself. He read the final line of his deliberations out over and over again, vowing never to forget it.

"It's not what you currently do, or what happens to you, that sets your course through life; It's what you think about yourself and your reaction to the changes that impact upon you, that ultimately control your destiny.......'

He closed his book and ran his fingers slowly over the slightly raised surface of his golden inscription.

Eight

He sensed that he had the solution to managing change, but like all true analytical thinkers he needed to know why the solution worked. In the same way that the medical profession are not content with knowing that a simple Aspirin aides well being. He was not content that his simple statement was a panacea for managing change.

He needed to know why it worked. What were the ingredients? Where did you get them from? What dosage was required? At what age should the treatment begin? Prevention was surely better than cure.

"I'm freezing, do you mind if I rest on top of your teapot for a while Bradley?" Elizabeth flew in through the open window and settled down on the lid of the bright yellow teapot, sitting only millimetres away from where a small hole served to vent the steam. Bradley mused that the colour of his teapot wasn't unlike the backing board he had chosen for her frame and she did look rather good against this background. Never the less he much preferred to have her alive and kicking.

"I've been thinking about this whole area of perception Elizabeth, and I've come to the conclusion that you're right, but I'm confused about where the whole thing stems from in the first instance."

"I thought you'd never ask," Elizabeth replied as she moved away from the steam hole and repositioned herself on the incline of the spout.

"It begins at the beginning. When I was sat in my egg I didn't know anything about anything. I had some basic genetic characteristics and instincts, but apart from that I was wholly uneducated and oblivious to pretty much everything.

As a caterpillar I started to observe what went on around me, and in a way I became a mini computer, hungry for input and instructions. These basic instructions came through experience of life. For example, my friend being captured by the bird, and through association with other caterpillars, who passed on their experiences.

As I grew my observation skills became more refined and I developed the ability to think and reason for myself as opposed to simply accepting any and every type of input as being correct. I also began to question the quality of this input. In a way I was developing character and personality. I was becoming an individual.

In my cocoon, my time capsule that would propel me from childhood to adulthood, I had time to make some kind of sense out of these various learning experiences and this is when I decided upon the type of butterfly I wanted to be. The Arctic butterfly. From what I had heard it displayed many of the characteristics and attitudes that I personally felt were important, and I decided that was the butterfly for me.

Although I appeared outwardly to be relatively mature and capable of rational thought, I was obviously still naive. There were quite clearly many things I still did not know and understand. This is quite a paradox because put bluntly - you don't know what you don't know.

That meant that the only data I had to go on was that derived from my observations of, and from my association with, others. My perception of both the world and of myself was based upon my experience of the world to date. That's where the problems started. The input, the data I had been fed, was incomplete and inaccurate. I had learned and experienced enough to decide what kind of butterfly I wanted to be - and then I had simply stopped learning.

I had been led to believe, by caterpillars that knew little more than I did about life, that I had the freedom of choice. I could choose what kind of butterfly I wanted to be - they said that if I thought about something often enough, held a clear vision of it in my mind's eye, and pursued it with all my heart, it would ultimately become me. They had heard two people discussing this very thing on a park bench in the garden of the local business school one day, and assumed that it applied to all of God's creations. They didn't consider the possibility that it only applied to human beings. So there it was. I had inaccurate data to work from, and I based my perception of the person I wanted to be on that data. Someone else had taken control of my thoughts and ideas and I didn't even realise it was happening."

Bradley's thoughts immediately went back to that fateful day at the career's convention when he had been fed what he now considered to be incomplete data. He had been told that the answer to successful adulthood was a trade and a good secure job at the end of it. He didn't really blame his father, or the career's officer for this because they were only advising him to the best of their knowledge, in much the same ways as Elizabeth's contemporaries had advised her.

The problem stemmed from the fact that they had also stopped learning. They refused to accept that the times were changing. Rapid technological advances were bringing new communications systems, transmitting information faster than ever before to every corner of the globe. The growing population, the post war baby boom and the incredible advances in computer science were to make such a difference to the world in which we lived.

They had chosen to live in the woodlands, they had chosen to ignore change and they perceived this strategy to be all that was needed to stem the constant flow of challenges that the inevitable change would bring.

"Bradley, are you paying attention?" She sensed that his thoughts were drifting but she also understood that he would be drawing parallels with his own life. At least she hoped he was.

"Sorry Elizabeth, some of these things are really hitting home." She smiled at his honesty and continued on.

"I've already explained my feelings of disappointment when I saw my reflection in the lily pond. Everything I had hoped and dreamed for had been taken away from me. I felt as though my very existence had been a lie. My perception of myself, my frame of reference of my entire world had been incorrect. I had been living a life based upon a false assumption, an incorrect perception, a piece of bad data, and I was shattered. I was in the wrong habitat, a product of my environment and my past programming and there was nothing I could do to change that."

"You said a product of your past programming Elizabeth, what do you mean by that ?"

"I mean that's where it all begins Bradley. It begins with the input, the data that we take on board, it's quality, it's accuracy, it's frequency and timeliness and it's purity. I had been programmed by my contemporaries to believe that I could be an Arctic Clouded Yellow butterfly. I had been programmed incorrectly and as a consequence I received incorrect results. You have been programmed since you emerged from your mother's womb in all manner of ways. Your parents, teachers, contemporaries, favourite movie stars, favourite footballers and rock bands, newspapers, books, casual acquaintances, advertising executives, neighbours, magazines and so on.

The list is endless. The speed at which you are bombarded with information and the quantity and quality of that information is really quite staggering. It is therefore not a good idea to blame yourself entirely when you make a wrong decision. I'm not saying you should blame someone else either, but you should come to terms with the fact that you are after all human and will from time to time make a mistake.

I do not blame my caterpillar friends for giving me wrong input, I blame myself for choosing to believe what I so desperately wanted to believe. If I'm being entirely honest there was a small part of me that knew there were some inconsistencies in their argument. For example, how could I enter into my cocoon in the garden and emerge from it in the mountains? I refused to give this perfectly good logistical question the time of day because I didn't want to believe anything other than what I was being told. Therefore, when I emerged as a Peacock butterfly, and when I had got over my initial disappointment, I had to start being honest with myself. The realisation of the thing I had tried to ignore. Above all else I was a product of my environment and I could do nothing to change that.

The good news is Bradley, that you can. You have the power and the God given ability to rise above your environment if you so desire. You have the ability to be a catalyst for change not merely a victim of that change and you also have that great personal freedom that I do not - you have the freedom to choose which one you would like to be. The catalyst or the victim. It's your choice Bradley."

Elizabeth could see that Bradley's attention was still drifting and she didn't want to start teaching him how to be a catalyst for change until he was in the right frame of mind. He didn't even notice that she had stopped talking, so she decided to take a well deserved snooze on the nice warm spout.

As Bradley sat deep in thought he wondered how his wife Susan and son William were getting on. They were four days into a family skiing holiday, except they didn't actually go as a complete family. Daddy was at home. He couldn't justify taking the time off at present because there was just too much going on at work. They considered postponing the trip, but they'd done that twice already and William would be back at school in a week's time. He missed them desperately, so much more than he had expected to and pondered on that well worn truism, 'you don't always appreciate what you have until it's too late'.

Not going on the trip with them was a perfect example of him visiting the woodlands, whilst they were visiting Austria. Elizabeth said that the inhabitants of the woodlands ignored change because it represented a state of imperfection. Something that might upset their routine and require them to be more flexible. He chose to ignore the fact that they had been promising to take William away for the last three years; that they hadn't infact even had a day out together that didn't involve going to the supermarket since their day trip to Blackpool two years ago, and that Susan had lost both her parents in the last eighteen months and desperately needed a break and a change of scenery.

It came as quite a shock when she announced they were going without him, but when he got used to the idea he was looking forward to being on his own so that he could catch up on the ever growing mountain of paper that lived in his in-tray. With hindsight, which is always perfect vision, he reasoned that he should have handled it differently. If only he'd planned things out better and co-operated with Susan instead of just ignoring her request he was sure he could have found a way to get round things.

It would have been more appropriate if, in Elizabeth's terms, he'd chosen to visit the desert and looked for a solution based upon co-operation rather than avoidance.

His actions had actually forced Susan into Rainforest mode. He had forced her to take aggressive action to implement her plans and he knew that although she had stuck to her guns, she would not be enjoying the holiday as much as if he had been there. He now concluded from his own experience that visiting the rainforest can be an effective way of getting what you want, Susan had got the holiday, but there would invariably be a price to pay in one form or another. If only you could have hindsight in advance, he thought. He could understand why Elizabeth wanted to live in the Arctic. A habitat or environment that was synonymous with leadership. The ability to unify everyone around a shared vision and turn that vision into a reality. In all honesty he had spent many years 'day tripping', visiting the various habitats from his weekday home in the garden or his weekend retreat in the woodlands.

Acceptance or avoidance - they were the two tools with which he had shaped his environment for as long as he could remember. They were his two characteristic responses to the onset of change. Accept it or avoid it.

He sensed however that it was time to become the master of change and the architect of his environment as opposed to simply living in an environment designed by someone else.

He was now beginning to understand what Elizabeth meant when she talked of being a product of her environment. She had no choice but to live in the garden, but every human being does have that choice.

Bradley opened his 'Imagineering' book at a clean page and selected his blue fountain pen from the container on the kitchen dresser. He knew he would need to refer to the rest of his discussions with Elizabeth many times in the future and he didn't want to risk missing any of the information.

"Do you remember when I said I spent some time in the garden of a psychology teacher last week?" Elizabeth started the discussion with a question, which gave her time to yawn and stretch, then she repositioned herself inside one of the freshly cut carnations that were arranged neatly in the vase on the table.

"Yes, I remember. You said he was giving additional lessons to some of his students."

"That's right, well done." Elizabeth replied in a patronising but humorous tone.

"It was actually three weeks ago now I come to think about it. His name was Dr. Winner and he was giving a series of additional lectures which he called 'Living in the Arctic'. The basic subject of the lectures was personal leadership, or as he called it leadership of self, with particular emphasis on leadership of self through times of change."

"Didn't you find it quite ironic that he chose to refer to his lectures as 'Living in the Arctic'?" Bradley couldn't help interrupting, he personally found it rather spooky, never mind ironic.

"The first time I heard him say it I almost fell off the rose bush," she replied, "but when I heard him explain the basis for his title I began to understand, and infact I began to feel quite proud in an odd sort of way.

He said that self leadership was the key to life itself. The ability to inspire, motivate and direct yourself was the ultimate of all abilities. Self leadership required discipline, commitment and a host of other qualities and guiding principles that you choose to live your life by.

He said that whilst everyone had access to the teachings and knowledge and opportunities that could help them to become anything they wanted to be in life, not everyone would whole heartedly grasp the nettle of self leadership."

"Those are very wise and reassuring words Elizabeth but what's any of this got to do with the Arctic?"

"Quite simply Bradley, the Arctic is a lonely and solitary place. A harsh environment where only the strong and determined survive.

He likens the Arctic to the leadership of self because the habitat of a leader is also at times a solitary place. Not a sad place, not a boring and uneventful place, but at times a solitary place. A place where you can withdraw deep inside yourself and find the inner strength that we all have in abundance, but for one reason or another fail to find.

This idea of solitude then formed the basis for the first of his four lectures - the lecture on Insight."

Bradley understood the sentiment of the Arctic but still found it slightly coincidental. Maybe things would become clearer as they went along. He sensed there was much more to Elizabeth than a brightly coloured set of wings and a few strong opinions.

"What are the other four lectures all about?" Bradley asked. He wasn't so much interested in knowing everything in advance, he simply wanted to make his notes look orderly by listing all the headings at the start and then detailing them individually afterwards.

This was the way he always structured his project files and he couldn't be expected to change everything he did all at once, even if this was his Imagineering book. Surely there must be some things he's currently doing correctly !

Elizabeth replied without question or comment as though she understood what he was about to do.

"Have you ever looked in the mirror and started to move your head closer and closer to the glass until the picture becomes distorted ?"

"Yes, I did it last week when I was trying to zero in on a grey hair that was growing out of my nose." Elizabeth wasn't particularly amused by Bradley's answer and resisted trying to visualise the scene as she carried on.

"Sometimes when you do that you get the illusion that you have several eyes, three, four, five or even more."

Bradley nodded in agreement as he thought back to his childhood days when he used to play a similar game by staring at his friends face until a giant eye appeared in the centre of his head like a scary monster.

"Butterflies and moths actually have thousands of eyes that we call 'ommatidia' and each eye forms a small picture. Our brain then puts all the pictures together. This gives us much better vision than if we just had two eyes, and that's why it's really hard to sneak up on us. In much the same way, the foundational concept of Dr Winners lecture's is 'increased vision'.

It's about seeing things through different eyes and It's about you as an individual.

If you actually had four physical eyes, for example, your vision would be increased tremendously. Just like my many eyes allow me to sense the presence of an intruder before their attack is close enough to be a threat, thus allowing me to react accordingly, your additional eyes would allow you to sense the onset of change before it was close enough to be a threat to you.

Obviously this is a hypothetical analogy, because you don't actually have four physical eyes, so Dr Winner has built his 'Living in the Arctic' lectures around the four hypothetical *I's* of;

Insight
Input
Intrinsic value
Intrepidness

Nine

*I*nsight.

"We'll start by going back to the mirror Bradley. Back to your perception of yourself. The way you see yourself is the first vital factor in the area of self leadership. In a rapidly changing society it is very easy to get left behind, particularly if you perceive yourself as being incapable of handling that change or not bright enough to understand new advances in technology and so on. Put bluntly, in order to fully understand change, you first need to fully understand yourself.

You need to recognise and understand your strengths, weaknesses, hopes and fears and the only way that recognition can take place is by taking a long hard look in the mirror. I'm going to fly around the garden now and strengthen my wings. Whilst I'm gone you can start to strengthen your self belief by doing a little homework. On four separate pages of your imagineering book you need to make four separate headings.

Strengths, Weaknesses, Hopes, and Fears. Then under each heading I want you to list as many things as possible that you feel about yourself under those headings.

For example, under strengths you should have things like smart in appearance, healthy, good looking, organised, able to drive, able to read and write, able to count, reliable, loyal, determined, persistent, well mannered, caring, optimistic, and so on. In other words don't hold back. It's vitally important that you assess yourself to the full.

Most people are so much better and have so much more going for them than they actually realise but they let the negativity of their surroundings filter out their recognition of their true value. This is your chance to describe your true value. Don't be modest, be truthful, but let that truth be an uninhibited truth, not one that is filtered by some other person's opinion.

Next we come to the weaknesses. This is not intended to be a negative thing, but a positive way forward. Once you recognise your weaknesses for what they are you can do something about them. This list will include things like being impatient, being a bad time keeper, constantly putting yourself down, allowing other people to dump all their problems on you and so on. Take your time with these because some things that appear to be a strength are actually a weakness. Let's take my last example of letting people dump all their problems on you. To have a good heart and want to help your fellow human being is undeniably a strength, but to take on all their problems and make them your own is an equally big weakness.

The real strength comes in helping them to develop a solution focus and having an empathetic rather than sympathetic viewpoint. Once someone conquers their own problem their perception of their ability to handle problems increases and the next time a problem occurs they are not as daunted or challenged by it.

I guarantee you that the list of strengths will far outweigh the list of weaknesses, but even if it didn't, which is purely hypothetical because it will, even if you only had one strength listed on that page, that one positive affirmation is all you would need to build upon. That's how strong the human spirit really is. One strand of hope, one ray of positive light can form the foundation of untold success.

Next you can move onto the page headed Hope. These are your aspirations, your desires for the future and they can be as small and insignificant or as large and mind expanding as you care to make them. The is your book of Imagineering, so make this your page of imagination.

Approach this list with one thought in mind. What would you hope for if you knew you couldn't fail to achieve it.

Finally complete the exercise by writing down your fears. What concerns you. A nuclear war, going to the toilet and discovering there's no paper left, daring to hope and then being let down if things don't go according to plan.

However irrational it may seem, make a note of it. Get those fears out into the open because once you recognise them, their power over you has already started to be drained. When I come back we'll discus the root of these perceptions and discuss how we can build on the strengths, balance out the weaknesses, realise the hopes and demolish the fears."

On that note Elizabeth flew off through the kitchen window and began to fly round and round the garden as fast as she possibly could do.

Bradley took up the fountain pen, filled it with blue ink and began to take that long hard look into the mirror.

Strengths

Weaknesses

Hopes

Fears

78

Elizabeth flew back into the kitchen just as Bradley finished and had stood up to close the window. The early evening air was starting to get chilly and he thought she had probably found somewhere warm to hide away for the evening.

"Golly I'm exhausted," she exclaimed as she lay flat out on the top of the wooden fireplace. She instantly began to cough as the smoke from the newly lit fire bellowed out from the hearth. The chimney was still cold and not yet working to its full capacity.

"Have you finished your lists?" She wasn't wasting any time.

"Yes. I've finished the list and you were quite right. There are some strengths there that seemed so obvious that I never really considered them to be strengths, and they certainly do outweigh the weak points." Bradley was quite inspired by the unearthing of his hidden strengths.

"Good, then let's move on. Now you have a full insight or perception of yourself. These perceptions have been developed through the various inputs that you have received since the day you were born. When a change comes along it's effects will more than likely spill over into each of the four areas of strength, weakness, hope and fear and depending upon which area it impacts on the most, this will dictate how you handle that change.

For example, if one of your fears is that a change in the manager at work will result in you being less appreciated, unless you have an opposing strength which says you are very good at your job, and unless that strength is your more dominant thought, there is a very great chance that when this change occurs your fear will be manifested.

It's not the easiest of concepts to get to grips with but it's back to the idea of the self fulfilling prophesy. You will gravitate towards your most dominant thoughts. In this example of the new boss, when he or she arrives, if the fear of being unappreciated is the dominant thought, then your subconscious will start to seek out any opportunity to confirm that belief.

Let's say the new boss is actually better at praising good work than the old one, but one day he's so busy that he forgets to express his appreciation for a great job you've done. Your subconscious will immediately pick up on that event, match it with your expectation and bingo - the prophesy is fulfilled and the fear is realised.

The primary activity of your mind must be to focus on your strengths and your hopes, the positive and uplifting thoughts, rather than on the weaknesses and fears, the negative and disheartening thoughts.

When a change enters your world you can then evaluate it and chose to accept or reject it on a positive basis. Put simply, you cannot always control the change but you can control the effect it has on you based upon the way you perceive it.

Let's take another example. When I changed into a Peacock butterfly I had no control over that change whatsoever. I had a fear that I may not become an Arctic Clouded Yellow, because I had a thought at the back of my mind that I couldn't enter my cocoon in the garden and emerge from it in the mountains. I think I told you about this earlier." Bradley nodded in silence.

"I was then faced with a choice. Change had entered my world and my worst fear had been realised. The temptation to jump off the lily and submerge myself in the pond water was very strong but as I stared into the water at my reflection, I couldn't help thinking that I looked rather nice.

I had beautiful colouring and exquisite markings. I was strong and had the ability to fly high above the flowers. The nectar was sweet and abundant. In other words I instinctively looked to my strengths. I couldn't control the change but I could control my response. That is such a blindingly simple truth that you must never forget Bradley.

Whatever changes come your way in the future, great or small, painful or pleasurable, always remember that ultimate freedom. The freedom to choose your response.

Earlier in the day you quoted Shakespeare, not fully understanding the depth of his words. Now I quote it back to you in the knowledge and comfort that this time you can comprehend the full import of the message he is conveying to his reader;

'Nothing is either good or bad, only thinking makes it so'.

Good night Bradley."

Ten

The following morning Bradley was up early. He wanted to review his notes before Elizabeth arrived and in particular he wanted to go over his list of strengths and hopes. He instinctively bypassed the list of weaknesses and fears. For now it was enough to know he had some and he had a suspicion that Elizabeth would know an antidote for the ills that they caused.

Speaking of antidotes he poured himself a large cup of black coffee and a large tumbler of ice water. Again he had overdosed on his red medicine but he was so enthused with his new found strengths that he found it virtually impossible to sleep without the restful influence of the grape. He considered adding another weakness to his list but had second thoughts and added a strength instead, 'socialises well'. This simple action brought a smile to his face.

He had instinctively looked at one of his character traits and chosen to see it as a strength and not a weakness. He had turned a negative into a positive and felt proud that he was starting to develop the habit of thinking positive and uplifting thoughts. Elizabeth was pleased to see he was ready and suggested that he made a new heading.

*I*nput.

"Your perception of yourself, and infact everything around you is a direct result of the input you have received. Remember, I thought I could be any type of butterfly I wanted to be, because of the incorrect input from my friends.

There are three sources of input that we need to be aware of. The external world as a whole, our internal world, and our experience. The external world is the most obvious because it provides us with everything from newspapers and television programmes to books and association and it's many facets combine to have a very strong influence upon us. The external world bombards us with input for every waking minute of the day and it is vital that we learn to handle this input in the right way.

When I talk about the programming we receive from our internal world, I'm referring in essence to our self talk.

When we sleep we are protected from the input of the external world, but our internal input goes on every second of our lives. Try to close your eyes for thirty seconds and think about nothing at all. It's impossible, you can't do it. You can't resist talking to yourself. No one is ever truly alone, at worst they have their thoughts to keep them company.

The third source of input is our experience. Experience is a great teacher and a great way to develop our perceptions. When we receive a piece of information our brain tries to attach that information to any others that correspond with it, that relate to a similar subject or idea, and over time builds up a more complete picture of that particular subject.

As change comes along we feed the elements of that change into our mind and they to attach themselves to the relevant inputs stored away in our vast databank. For example, as a child you were warned that the porcelain bricks of the gas fire are very hot and you should not touch them. One day you're rolling around on the floor fascinated by their orange glow and you put your finger just a little too close - the experience of burning your finger now combines with the warning message from your parents and even as an adult you are now very wary of touching the porcelain bricks.

Your inner voice, your self talk tells you to stay well away. In other words you have learned through both theory and practice that it's not a good idea.

This is a simple example, but it illustrates the point just as well as a complicated one. You are reacting based upon experience. You are living out of your memory.

This is of course a very safe way to live, but like all other safe courses of action it has the capacity to result in inaction.

You may be reluctant to remove the bricks for cleaning even when they are cold.

The proverbial cat that sat on a hot tin roof never sits on a cold one again either. In other words a response based purely upon memory is likely to imprison you to a life in the garden. To handle change effectively you need to develop the ability to not only live out of your memory but to also live out of your imagination. The ability to be proactive and seek a solution rather than merely being reactive and doing nothing. The ability to take action.

Your past input or programming may have left you with many legacies, many thoughts and ideas that prevent you from being proactive. Your early failures at learning a musical instrument may dissuade you from ever trying again. Your failure to get promoted in the last company reorganisation may instil you with terror because there's another reshuffle around the corner and you expect to suffer again.

Your failure in your own business may result in you turning down any future business propositions on the basis that you failed to succeed last time. You decide that maybe you were born to work for someone else. The chances are great however that there were many more factors involved in your past failures than you choose to admit.

A bad music teacher or the choice of the wrong instrument, internal company politics that fail to recognise ability and appoint on a more political basis, or a very difficult economic climate that hit your market sector particularly hard. Whatever the reason for living out of your memory, it is essential to your healthy growth and development that you constantly take on board new data, to help balance out the old data and past experiences.

Dr Winner recommends that the new data should be predominantly positive and should be gleaned from a variety of sources. Autobiographies of successful people, books on positive thinking, audio learning programmes of individuals that are achieving things in your area of interest, and through association with positive and successful people.

He cites this association factor as a vital ingredient in the management of change. There is something very powerful about meeting and talking to people who have undergone change that is similar in nature to that which you are experiencing yourself. Similarly, there is something just as powerful about associating with people that have failed to handle change and have developed a very negative or defeatist attitude. Whenever possible it is advisable to give them a wide birth. Remember Bradley, no one ever erected a monument to a failure.

You may at times have difficulty in sourcing all the positive and uplifting input that you need so it is a very good idea to also prepare your own material. Developing simple self talk statements that focus on your strengths and hopes are a very powerful way to help you through times of change and help you to live out of your imagination. Even the simple action of reading the list of strengths and hopes that you wrote earlier can have a marked effect upon your confidence.

*I*ntrinsic value.

This is the value of self, or self esteem. The identification of your strengths is intended to enhance your feeling of self worth, your recognition that you are a person of value. Positive input and association with people that have experienced the challenges and growing pains that you are encountering subsequently adds to this feeling of self worth. What you then need is constant reinforcement both in the form of positive self affirmation and physical achievement, the latter ideally resulting in some kind of recognition.

Your ability to handle change is directly related to your feeling of self worth and that relationship makes this a very important area to concentrate on. Dr Winner said that in his opinion one of the biggest difficulties facing people in their quest for enhanced self esteem is the pace at which they are currently living their lives at, and the feelings of stress that go along with it. The constant pressures within society to perform at an increasingly higher level, and the corresponding feelings of rejection and lack of control are eroding peoples self esteem on a daily basis.

British life in the 1990's is characterised by long working hours, fear of redundancy, large mortgages, negative equity, long stressful car journeys and so on, all of which compound that feeling of being out of control. How can you keep your employer, your customers, your employees, and your bank manager happy? How can you juggle all the elements of your life, meet all your responsibilities and still keep a grip on your sanity?

If peoples self talk, their daily in depth conversation with themselves, is characterised by all these questions and negative reactions it's no wonder that they are feeling stressed. It's very difficult to have a strong and positive self image when you feel like such a victim of your circumstances and environment

It's true that a certain amount of stress is required to stimulate action but too much can lead to insomnia, tension, and ultimately physical and mental illness. Each year an estimated six million people consult their doctors because they feel depressed and anxious and equally as many suffer symptoms of stress related illness but do not seek medical advice. Both my body and yours are designed to respond to stress in a physical manner with our primitive 'fight or flight' instincts.

Our bodies prepare themselves for increased physical exertion and even if the threat is only an emotional one rather than a physical one, our subconscious mind cannot tell the difference between an imagined and a real event.

That means that the same responses go on inside us even if we only imagine a situation of conflict. Ultimately, prolonged stress will take its toll on organs and systems within the body and physical illness will undoubtedly follow.

As your feeling of well being reduces, it is very probable that your daily conversations with yourself will also deteriorate as you tell yourself the job is making you ill, you cannot cope with the demands of your family and so on.

We now have a situation where your self esteem, your intrinsic value, is at rock bottom. In this state of mind your ability to handle any more change, no matter how small, is virtually nil. You are most likely to either retreat to the garden - accepting everything that is thrown at you - or hide in the woodlands - ignoring everything and mostly everyone around you.

There are several books that have been written about stress and there are several techniques you can learn to help you combat its symptoms. Preserving a social life, taking an annual holiday, exercising regularly, discussing your state of mind with a close friend, planning ahead, generally improving your time management and so on.

These techniques are very effective and are worth adopting, but Dr Winner argues that they are to a degree 'quick fixes'. In medical terms they deal with cure rather than prevention.

Conversely, developing a healthy self image, a feeling of intrinsic value, is more akin with long term prevention. If your feeling of self worth is high, your daily conversations will stay positive and you will develop a solution focus to the changes that impact upon you."

As Elizabeth paused for a drink of nectar Bradley thought back to his situation with the family holiday. He clearly recalled a conversation he had with himself last week. 'If I take a holiday now it might be seen by the boss that I can't cope with the pressures of my job. He might think that maybe I'm not the right person to head up the new quality team and whilst I'm away Jones will have a chance to make a good impression. What if I'm not as well thought of as I imagined? Maybe the quality of my last two projects could have been a little better, maybe they could have been finished earlier and been more under budget.'

He quickly flicked back the pages of his book to his list of strengths and read the first three out loud. ' I am an excellent project manager - The last project I ran was the most successful the company has ever had in terms of both profitability and time management - I have a better understanding of the requirements of the new quality job than Jones will ever have.'

Those were not boastful words, they were words imparted to him by the board of directors during the post appraisal meeting of his last project. How soon he had forgotten. How soon he had allowed the stressful environment he was in to undermine his feeling of self worth. How he wished he had written that list of strengths, and read it daily, the week before Susan booked the holiday. How he will never make that mistake again.

"So, are you starting to get the picture about the power of the words that you say to yourself Bradley?" At first he answered with a silent nod, but then felt the need to probe deeper.

"Yes Elizabeth, I'm getting there, but isn't this partly a case of resting on your past laurels?"

"Good point," Elizabeth replied with an air of expectancy for the question. "The past is the starting point. A list of your current strengths is the foundation upon which you can start to rebuild your self esteem and shape your environment but as your rightly observe, life is about moving on.

Eleven

Intrepidness.

"To be intrepid is to be fearless, and the fear of change is conquered by knowledge and action. The recognition of your strengths and past successes gives you that foundational knowledge, and action in the direction of your future hopes completes the pincer movement - it's a two pronged attack on your fears.

The leadership of self is the true expression of personal freedom and every human being has the choice to exercise that freedom. To lead yourself you need to understand where you want to go in the various areas of your life, and be intrepid on your journey. We said earlier that when change enters your life it spills over into each of the four areas of strengths, weaknesses, hopes and fears. Once this happens it is up to you to choose how you will lead yourself through that change. Which habitat you will choose."

Bradley immediately thought back to the job of Quality manager and his initial reaction. When he heard that the job was up for grabs he initially greeted this potential change with great concern.

It impacted much more on the area of his fears than his strengths and his reaction had been to run into the rainforest. In other words he was overly forceful in his pursuit of the job by working harder than ever and sacrificing his precious family time resulting in him missing the holiday. Such was his fear of being passed by for promotion. He no longer blamed himself for this, and had already started planning to make amends.

He recognised that this was an inevitable reaction borne out of his negative self talk as a result of his increasingly stressed state of mind. The correct choice would have been to visit the Arctic. To pursue the opportunity in a planned, logical and positive way. Had he recognised that the job opportunity actually impacted more on his list of strengths rather than his list of fears, the trip to the Arctic would have been the natural choice. This realisation was a very powerful and personal confirmation of the great importance of focusing on his strengths rather than his weaknesses.

"The habitat that you choose," Elizabeth continued, "will be determined by the relative importance of that change, and the impact it is likely to have upon your life.

You need to assess this importance fully, and subsequently decide what action to take. To visit the garden and accept it, hide in the woodlands and ignore it, take cover in the mountains and fight it, stroll through the desert hand in hand with it, charge into the rainforest and pursue It aggressively at any price or soar high in the Arctic sky and proactively lead yourself through it. You then need to have a set of guidelines for your life. Not a rigid set of rules that you would never bend, unfortunately life is not predictable enough to allow that, but a flexible set of guidelines that define your character and your perceived purpose in life."

"You mean like a changeless core," Bradley shouted out.

"Dr Winner couldn't have put it better himself," Elizabeth replied.

"A changeless core." Throughout my development from the egg to the caterpillar to the pupa to the butterfly I underwent many physical and emotional changes but my central core, my abdomen and thorax remained with me.

We can liken this central core in me to the central core of principles and values in a human being. The things that remain constant in times of change. The unvarying central core that is essential if a healthy and productive life is to be maintained when change occurs."

Bradley immediately thought back to his apprenticeship and the relentless mopping of the nice clean workshop floors. His instructors had been trying to teach him about persistence and discipline and tried to instil these values in him from an early stage. It also amused him that he was witnessing the manifestation of something that Elizabeth had said earlier. She said that when you receive a piece of new data your brain tries to attach it to a similar strand of information that it may already have in store. The thought process that he had just gone through, interlinking the memory of his apprenticeship with her theory of a changeless core confirmed her teachings very well.

What amazed him more than anything was the speed at which his mind had made that connection given that it had over forty years of memories to sift through. He turned back to his list of strengths and added a new one. 'I truly am an amazing creation'.

"It's very difficult to give this changeless core a name," she said very thoughtfully. "In a way it's your character, but that doesn't go far enough. It's the foundation of everything you think about, everything you believe in, everything you dream of and desire and it's that intangible and much thought about concept of 'the will to live'. Can you think of a name for all that rolled into one?" She asked - without the answer in mind. It was important that this was the answer of a human being.

"It's me," Bradley replied almost instantly."It's me."

Elizabeth raised her head, she was expecting several minutes of silence and deep thought so that she could have a quick fly around the garden. She still had twenty more laps to do to meet her daily goal. "What do you mean it's you?" She asked.

"No, not you," Bradley replied, "me". He knew what she meant but couldn't miss the opportunity to have a little fun with her.

"It's me Elizabeth. If I'm to lead me I need to understand me and know where me wants to go and what me is prepared to do, or not do, to get there."

"Perfect," Elizabeth replied. "Now you need to think in detail about you. I suggest you start by writing a list of things that are most important to you in life. Let's say the top thirty, and number them in order of priority. Then write a second list which outlines the things you want to achieve in each of those areas in the next twelve months.

Following on from these two you then need to produce a third list. This is a list of actions that you need to take in order to achieve the things on the second list thus allowing you to make progress in the priority areas of your life that you identified on the first list. Don't worry, I'll give you an example of this in a minute to make things clearer. Next you need to take your diary out and plan in sufficient time to ensure that the list of actions gets done.

This exercise will take a lot of thought and a lot of planning but its value cannot be overstated. This is taking a proactive approach to your life. This is the basis for living out of your imagination and being able to have hindsight in advance."

Bradley stopped writing as he heard this closing phrase.

It was a phrase he had conjured up in his thoughts yesterday, but had not shared with Elizabeth. She ignored his surprised expression, having no desire to discuss what she knew he was thinking, and she continued.

"Finally, once your action plan is written firmly into your diary you need to set a standard for your beliefs. In other words you need to identify the key elements of your changeless core. Before you get started I'll give you a very personal example. The things that are most important to me in life, the things that would be on my first list if I could write, in order of priority are:

1. To reproduce
2. To pass on what I have learned
3. To drink the nectar of the finest flowers
4. To enjoy the long hot summer days

I know it's a small list, but don't forget I'm a butterfly. If I could drive a Ferrari it would be on the list. If I could fly to the Arctic it would be on the list. If I could drive a car in the Monaco grand prix it would be on the list. If I could go shopping in New York it would be on the list. I think you get the picture. Remember, I'm a product of my environment." Bradley nodded and began to jot down ideas for his own list.

"Now I'll tell you what I want to achieve in each of these areas in the next twelve months. This is my second list.

My first priority is to reproduce and the things I want to achieve in this area are as follows.

- The father of my children must be an Arctic Yellow.
- My wings must be as strong as I can make them.
- My ability to withstand the cold must be maximised.

My second priority is to pass on what I have learned and the things I want to achieve in this area are as follows.

- Select a candidate to teach.
  Impart a little knowledge on him and test his ability.
- Help him or her to develop a clear understanding of Dr. Winners' principles.

I'm sure you're getting the picture so I won't talk about my third and fourth priorities, especially since they're a little self indulgent, and we'll go on to the third list. This is a list of actions you need to take to achieve the things on the second list, and to save time we'll just look at the actions associated with my first priority.

The priority was to reproduce and the three things that I want to achieve in that priority area in the next twelve months are to ensure the father is an Arctic Yellow, my wings are as strong as possible and I can withstand the cold as much as possible. To achieve these things I need to take the following actions:

- Identify a place in Britain where I can find an Arctic Yellow.
- Infiltrate that place.
- Strengthen my wings by completing twenty laps of a large garden every day for at least two months
- Build up my resistance to the cold by spending at least One hour per day in the coldest part of the garden.

All I have to do now is plan these actions into my diary and put in the effort in line with my defined standard of behaviour. I'll talk about that standard of behaviour when I come back, I need to do some more laps of the garden and you need to prepare your first three lists. See you later."

The things that are most important to me in life

The things I want to achieve in each area of importance - in the next twelve months

Action list

Action list

Twelve

By the time Bradley had finished his action list his wrist was aching from all the writing and his head was spinning from the thought of all the things he had to do. He contemplated the possibility that the list of actions could make him feel even more stressed than before and he was anxious to discuss this point with Elizabeth. He made himself a cup of coffee and some cheese on toast and placed a generous spoonful of strawberry jam on a saucer at the side of the flower vase. As Elizabeth entered the kitchen she flew instinctively to this energy sustaining mixture.

"Thanks Bradley, I needed that. If I'd known how good it tasted I would have put it on my list of priorities, but then again it's a good example to reinforce the point that you should never be too inflexible to embrace and capitalise upon an opportunity when it comes your way. It will be worth remembering this point as you transfer your action list into your diary and subsequently generate a daily task list. If you have things planned it is far easier to be flexible than if you have nothing planned because in this latter case you simply end up being reactive. Planning your diary around your priorities allows you to be proactive and live out of your imagination. It allows you to have that all important hindsight in advance because you are literally predicting your future."

"I greatly enjoyed the exercise Elizabeth and I understand the concept, but I'm concerned that this long list of actions and numerous diary entries will compound my feelings of being stressed out. Am I wrong?"

"Providing the actions are not too demanding and you are capable of achieving them there is no need to feel stressed or threatened by their existence. They actually serve as very positive stress reducers for three reasons.

Firstly, they give you a complete understanding of what you need to do to achieve your priorities and realise your dreams. The biggest cause of stress is the feeling of being out of control. What this action list does is put you very firmly in control by giving you the knowledge or know how to achieve those priorities.

Secondly, as you complete each action point you get an enhanced feeling of self esteem, a feeling that you have succeeded at something and taken a positive step towards making your priorities happen.

This is positive feedback and good experience and because your experiences play a vital role in creating your perceptions, your perception of yourself is enhanced.

Thirdly, they allow you to take an informed decision about the effects of any change that comes your way.

When change occurs you can analyse it, compare its effects with your action list and act accordingly. In a nutshell the change cannot control you. You become the catalyst rather than the victim.

I'll give you an example. Last week the garden I was living in was virtually destroyed by a fire as a result of the owner burning a pile of rubbish. The fire got out of control and soon it had swept through the dry grass and plants before he could do anything about it. An unexpected change had entered my life.

The friends that lived in the garden with me have no direction in their life. They have no concept of self leadership and they simply moved to the garden next door. The problem was that the flowers next door were of very low quality. The roses had never been pruned and greenfly ran amok. Referring to my mental list of actions I knew that I had to fly twenty laps of the garden daily and to sustain me to do that I had to have very good quality nectar.

I therefore took control of my life in the face of this unwanted change by making a decision based upon what was important to me in life. I took control by adopting the tactics of the rainforest. I moved aggressively to a new location. I would have preferred to have adopted the tactics of the Arctic, and planned my move by doing an advance survey of the area. I would have then gathered my friends and explained the full impact of their decision to move next door, said good-bye to those that chose to stay, led the others to a better place and so on, but in this instance it was not an option.

I had to move quickly to continue progressing towards my goals and priorities. I could not control the change but I could and did control my response to that change because I knew where I was going in life. I had developed self leadership."

"So the fact that you knew where you were going in life allowed you to select the most appropriate response to the change." Bradley thought she was just about to make that final comment but felt obliged to confirm she had his full attention. He remembered an old training course he'd been on at work. They called it 'active listening'.

"You've got it in one Bradley. That's why you shouldn't be daunted by the action list - it's your passport to your dreams. The other more unexplainable and intangible benefit to my move, and infact to most situations that you respond to in a proactive way, is that it resulted in even more benefits than I initially envisaged. It is often the case that great benefits come from great adversity and this is one very good reason why you need to balance this whole process out with that standard of belief that I talked about earlier. The garden that I selected was yours, and the additional benefit is that it also served to achieve another of my priorities i.e. to select a candidate to teach. In fact, now I come to think about it, the life threatening change of being caught was the catalyst for me to speak to you and the start of our friendship.

Victory snatched from the jaws of defeat - another good reason to have those standards of belief."

Bradley started to blush and become embarrassed about the way they had met. He decided to ask a question before she also had time to dwell on their eventful first meeting.

"What exactly do you mean by 'standards of belief' ?"

"It's the key elements of your changeless core. It's the backdrop against which you pursue your dreams and priorities. It's the attitude with which you approach everything that you do. Your attitude comes very close to being everything about success or failure. With the right attitude anyone can snatch victory out of the jaws of defeat regardless of their level of education or position in society.

Your attitude is basically the way you think and is normally referred to with some kind of prefix like good, bad, positive or negative. This is because your attitude is in a sense the thing that you display. It's the public manifestation of your private thoughts and it is borne out of your belief system. Once you have written your action list and planned your diary you are ready to set out and achieve your goals and dreams but in doing so you must have standards of belief that you will apply every step of the way. In a sense It's like having laws of the land for a country or codes of ethics within a company. Your standards of belief are your personal code of ethics, your internal attitudes that come together to form the external manifestation of you.

We can come up with hundreds of words, some very similar in meaning, to describe the standards of belief that an individual needs to have to succeed in life, and I'd encourage you to think about this subject in depth whenever you get the opportunity. For now I'm going to briefly describe the ones that Dr. Winner always used to quote, as being, in his humble opinion, the most important.

*S*elf Discipline.

Leadership of self requires discipline of self. The man who won't answer to the rudder will eventually answer to the rocks. Without this standard of behaviour you will never be successful. Self discipline is about forcing yourself to do the things that you know you should do, when you should do them, whether you like to do them or not. Successful people make a habit of doing the things that unsuccessful people are not prepared to do. In any generation only five percent of people realise their true potential, and the reason is simple.

Only five percent have the necessary self discipline.

We have a natural tendency to always do what is fun and relaxing rather than what is necessary for success. Self discipline is about identifying the line of least resistance and walking in the opposite direction. That is why my number one and number two priorities are to reproduce and to pass on what I have learned.

My third priority, to drink the nectar of the finest flowers combines both business and pleasure because the nectar is vital to my health to achieve priorities one and two but it's also very nice. My last priority, to enjoy the long hot summer days, represents the most self indulgent activity - the line of least resistance. Self discipline dictates that it will remain the last priority for the time being."

"I now understand the importance of self discipline Elizabeth," Bradley interrupted, "but how do people develop the motivation to develop the discipline?"

"Simple." She replied instantly as though expecting the question. They write a list of their strengths, which helps to build their self esteem, and they write a list of '*the things that are most important to me in life*' they write list number one. They think about their life in a proactive way, daring to live out of their imagination and daring to dream. Basically they identify their desires. **DISCIPLINE** is a:

Desire **I**nternalised **S**o **C**learly **I**t **P**revents **L**aziness
Inspiring **N**ecessary **E**ffort

That's why list number one is so vitally important. If you don't know where you're going you don't need discipline to help you get there.

*P*ersistence.

This is the next vital standard of belief and can best be described as 'self discipline in action'. Edison said that 'genius in one percent inspiration and ninety-nine percent perspiration'. You may have the self discipline to do something you don't want to do or are afraid to do, on one occasion, but what if you have to do it more than once?

What if you needed to do it ten or twenty or a hundred times? What if you needed to do it a thousand times, like Edison did to develop his light bulb, would you give up after nine, nineteen, ninety-nine or nine hundred and ninety nine times - not knowing that one more try would have done it? Persistence is about never giving up and is summed up by that timeless maxim 'if at first you don't succeed, try and try again'.

The history books are full of stories where victory was only achieved after great loss and through persistence and a refusal to quit. I recommend that you seek out the autobiographies of successful people and learn from their experiences. I guarantee you that a common thread running through the fabric of their lives will be their refusal to quit. Their persistent attitude. In the eyes of the world they failed many times, but in their eyes they had many opportunities from which to learn and gather experience. Experience is what you get when you don't get the result you want and the key to persistence is to learn from that experience and apply it in your next attempt to succeed. The experience will help you to bounce back stronger than ever.

Had I not been persistent in my attempts to escape your net I would have been hanging on your wall now instead of sitting on your teapot. If you ever consider quitting at anything I would encourage you to remember that."

Bradley smiled at her softly delivered rebuke as he framed his next question. "If list number one gives you the motivation to develop self discipline, what gives you the motivation to develop a persistent attitude - is that also list number one?"

"It's a combination of lists one, two and three," she replied. "Its a combination of the things that are most important to you, the things you want to achieve in each of those areas in the next twelve months and your daily action list. Your will to persist is partly a measure of and a function of your self belief. Failure reduces self belief so it is important that you break list one down into lists two and three because they are smaller, more achievable goals.

It is highly likely that even though you may on occasion fail to achieve something on list one at the first attempt, you will achieve something on list two or three.

This serves to reinforce your self belief and spur you on to the next attempt. It is therefore vitally important to look for the good in any result. No one ever hurt their eyes by looking on the bright side. That brings us nicely to the next standard of belief.

Optimism.

I have heard fellow butterflies complain that the roses have thorns, but I'm grateful that the thorns have roses.

Look for the good in every situation. Look for the valuable lesson that you can learn. Assume a cheerfulness you do not feel and soon you will feel the cheerfulness you assumed. To be optimistic is to have a solution focused attitude. You rarely get what you deserve but you always get what you expect and an attitude of optimism ensures that you expect good things and are far more likely to get them. This is back to the idea of the self fulfilling prophesy that we discussed earlier.

The body manifests what the mind harbours. Give your mind an instruction and it goes to work on it. Give it positive, optimistic instructions and it will manifest positive results. Give it negative and defeatist instructions and you'd better watch out ! Expect success and you're half way there. When people expect to fail they fail and that reinforces their original view that they are a failure.

When you team up self discipline and persistence with an expectation of good results you are invincible.

*H*onesty.

No matter how brilliant a man may be, he will never engender confidence in his subordinates or his associates if he lacks simple honesty and moral courage. Honesty pays Bradley, but it doesn't seem to pay enough for some people !

Honesty and integrity are critical and indispensable ingredients of success. It takes a lifetime of constant performance to build up a reputation of honesty and if you ever lose that reputation you will have to move a long way from home before you can ever do business again. The type of honesty that I'm referring to here is basic honesty related to other peoples money, property, business dealings and so on, but there is also honesty with self - a vital area that we must not ignore.

As you read the autobiographies of great men and women, and you associate with other successful people in your chosen field of endeavour, you will sometimes question who you are.

You may think you do not have the correct family background or education or residential status that is needed to succeed. You may compare yourself with these other individuals and try to adopt their characteristics, their style of dress, their way of life and so on. In my world this is called mimicry. In many locations, especially in tropical areas, edible butterflies have evolved wing patterns that mimic inedible species, thus gaining protection for themselves.

This is called Batesian mimicry, after its discoverer, the English naturalist and explorer Henry Bates. To a point this outer covering does the trick, but inside the butterflies are not what they pretend to be. They visit the watering holes of their adopted role models and eat nectar from the same flowers, but deep down inside they are in turmoil because they are living a double life. They are constantly suppressing their natural instincts to visit their native habitat, to go back to their roots and be themselves.

They are not being honest with themselves and this ultimately has a very damaging effect on their self esteem.

They have no real concept of who they are or what they stand for, and unless you stand for something Bradley, you will eventually fall for anything.

The leadership of self therefore requires the honesty of self. Be honest about who you are, what you are, where you come from and where you are going. Don't try to mimic those around you. Learn from them and emulate their success, even go as far as embracing their values and beliefs but always be yourself.

Always strive to be the best you - that you can be.

Loyalty.

To be loyal is to be firm in one's allegiance. To be firm in the support one gives to a cause. In today's society there are many causes that are constantly vying and competing for your support. Your job or business, your family, your church and so on. This is another reason why the lists you prepared earlier are so vitally important. They give you guidance and direction as to the areas that should be receiving your attention and support. Your loyalty is the thing that comes into question when any kind of distraction occurs and is a true reflection of your character. In marriage when a distraction occurs will you stay loyal? In business when an opportunity arises to gain short term benefit by jeopardising a long term relationship will you be loyal? In life, when you have identified the things you want and the way to get them honestly, will you allow yourself to be side tracked by some other scheme or will you be loyal?

The choice will always be yours Bradley, and at times it may be a difficult one, but there is no quicker way to destroy your self esteem, no quicker way to erode your feeling of intrinsic value, than to be disloyal. I once heard someone say that loyalty could be measured by thinking about what you would do, if you knew you would never be found out. In a sense that may be true but it ignores one vital element - the element of self. You would know what you had done - and you would have to live with that disloyal action for every waking moment of every day.

Above all Bradley, to thine own self be true, or as Theodore Roosevelt said '.. It is better to be faithful than be famous'.

Those are the five standards of behaviour that are key to your success Bradley. Self discipline, Persistence, Optimism, Honesty and Loyalty, but there is one more behaviour that Dr Winner talked about that is fundamental to life itself. We'll discuss that tomorrow."

After a light supper Bradley poured himself a small glass of red wine and once again sat staring into the flames. He missed Susan and William more than ever and he felt quite guilty at the way he had neglected them over the years. He turned back the pages of his imagineering book and wished he could turn back the pages of the last few years as easily. He instinctively stopped at list number one.

'The things that are most important to me in life - priority number one - to be the best husband and father that I can possibly be.' He turned next to his action list, took his diary out of his briefcase, blocked off the following week from Monday to Saturday, turned the diary on its side and wrote one word across the entire week - skiing !

As he poured a second glass of wine, not wishing this momentous occasion - the conscious start to a life of self leadership - to go without celebration, he reflected upon Elizabeth's list of priorities. She had been strengthening her wings and increasing her resistance to the cold as a prerequisite to having a family of her own. She also said she had to identify a place in Britain where she can find an Arctic Yellow and infiltrate that place.

Bradley suddenly realised what she was trying to do. She was developing her own cross breeding programme in the hope that one day her ancestors would be strong enough to make the journey all the way to the Arctic and once there, have the strength and resistance to the cold to survive there. He remembered how she told him that she tried so hard to make the journey herself but turned back only when death was imminent.

He thought at the time that she had given up on her dream but now he realised she had simply re-focussed her thoughts and developed a flexible plan. She had resigned herself to the fact that she was a product of her environment, but was determined to make a positive step forward in the direction of her dream. She was laying the foundations for her future generations to break free from that oppressive environment, if they so chose. She may have failed but she was determined to never be a failure.

She wanted to ensure that her future generations had the power of choice, just like his father had wanted to ensure that his son had greater choice than he had. Bradley reached up to the second shelf of his bookcase and selected a local guide book. He ran his finger down the index, smiling as he stopped half way down - 'Butterfly farm' - page sixteen.

The next morning Elizabeth arrived earlier than ever and Bradley was glad he'd reduced his medication to just two glasses. The funny thing was he slept better than ever. It felt as though now he knew where he was going in life, now he had embarked upon the journey of self leadership, he was more at peace with the world.

"O.K. Bradley, just one more thing to discuss then I have to go. I've got a busy day ahead of me. This morning we're going to talk about having a teachable spirit. This is the final ingredient. You have written the lists, you know where you're going, and you now have some standards of belief that you will always adhere to on your journey of self leadership. As you make that journey, as you make progress through life, life itself will also make progress.

New things will be invented, new ideas developed and theories produced. New role models will emerge, new mentors will enter your life and new challenges will hide around every corner. Today you are at the start of the most exciting adventure that ever was. You have the basic foundations, your dreams and your guiding principles, but they are only the foundations. As you build your life you need to build on your knowledge, to embrace the many new things that the world has to offer.

When change comes along you need to analyse it, test it against your action list, decide how to react to it based upon what it has to offer - and your understanding of the various habitats, and use that change to your advantage.

120

However, fear is a tenacious enemy and at times the onset of change will have the capacity to fill you with fear. You must therefore develop a teachable spirit. You must seek out knowledge at every opportunity. You must never miss or pass on the chance to grow mentally. To live you must constantly grow.

The ultimate aim in life is not in victory or defeat but in the perfection of the character of its participants.

Furthermore, determining your direction should never be left in the hands of someone else. That's just about all I can tell you Bradley The rest my dear friend is up to you."

"How long will it take you to get to the Butterfly farm ?"

Bradley sensed that the lecture was over, and Elizabeth smiled in silent recognition of his understanding of her next task.

"It's not the journey that's the challenge," she eventually replied, "they segregate the areas very well because of the different climates they need to maintain. The tricky part is getting into the right enclosure."

Now Bradley was smiling as he saw his opportunity to go some way towards thanking her for the priceless gift of life she had given to him.

"That's no challenge at all Elizabeth. I've always wanted to see an Arctic Clouded Yellow."

"Then what are we waiting for Bradley? Let's go !"

"Bradley are you aright? You've been staring at that picture frame for ages." The entrance of Bradley's secretary brought him back to reality as he turned to greet her.

"Yes, I'm fine Wendy. I was just thinking about an old friend." He hadn't had a secretary before, but his new job as quality manager was very demanding and he certainly needed one.

"I'm going to the theatre with Susan and William tonight so I'll be leaving at four. Can you make sure today's letters are ready for me to sign before I leave please."

"Yes, that's no problem," she replied, "what are you going to see?"

"I'll give you a clue Wendy. Here's a quote from the play.

'... nothing in life is good or bad, only thinking makes it so' ..."

As Wendy left the office Bradley turned again to the picture frame. He focused first on the yellow background and then the words in the foreground.

ME

I look in the mirror, and what do I see - a unique
creation, a winner - that's me

Beneath the confident exterior is a self leading
interior - I'm no longer inferior, I'm a winner -
that's me

I know where I'm going, my self disciplines
showing - I'm persistent and consistent, I'm a
winner - that's me

I'm honest and loyal and welcome life's toil
always looking on the bright side, I'm a winner -
that's me

My nature is such that I desire to learn much
I know that knowledge is vital, I'm a winner -
that's me

I know the world's changing, nothing ever stands
still - I welcome it, embrace it and control it at
will

I choose to be a catalyst - not a victim you see,
I'm leading my life, I'm a winner - that's me

I'm living to grow, and I'm growing to live, I'm
exercising my freedom, I'm a winner - that's me